In the hands
of the discoverer,
medicine becomes
a heroic art.

RALPH WALDO EMERSON

International Standard Book Number
ISBN-13: 978-0-9790827-0-2
ISBN-10: 0-9790827-0-6

Published by
Cleveland Clinic
9500 Euclid Avenue
Cleveland, Ohio 44195
www.ClevelandClinic.org

cleveland clinic

twoviews

PHOTOGRAPHS BY LARRY FINK AND ANDREW MOORE

A great medical center is more than buildings, people and technology. It is a repository of wisdom. A powerful engine of hope. No single point of view could ever capture its complexity. Its essence escapes the solitary eye. *Two Views* offers an alternative way of seeing. Two photographers. Two utterly different sensibilities. Larry Fink. Andrew Moore. Each comes to Cleveland Clinic with a fresh eye, at different hours, different seasons. Each applies his own aesthetic to the world-within-a-world that is Cleveland Clinic. Each complements and contrasts with the other. Their combined views create a unique book that reveals a specific period in time, yet whose concerns—health, compassion, the cycle of life—are timeless. *Two Views* gives us patient care, research and education at an institution whose home is in the here and now, but whose ultimate perspective is infinite.

two views

CLEVELAND CLINIC IS MANY THINGS TO MANY PEOPLE. TO PATIENTS, IT IS A BEACON OF HOPE AND HEALING. TO PHYSICIANS, IT IS A PLACE TO PRACTICE, DISCOVER AND TEACH. TO THE ARTIST PERMITTED TO ROAM ITS HALLWAYS, STUDY ITS BUILDINGS AND OBSERVE ITS PEOPLE, CLEVELAND CLINIC IS THE OPPORTUNITY OF A LIFETIME.

Cleveland Clinic is not only a major academic medical center and a national and international health resource; it is a front-row seat on the human condition. Enter the daily life of Cleveland Clinic and you plunge into the tide of existence. You feel the ebb and flow of sickness and health. You cherish vitality. You witness anxiety. You share the joy of lives saved and families restored.

This book is the inspiration of Delos M. Cosgrove, M.D., CEO and President of Cleveland Clinic and a distinguished cardiac surgeon. Dr. Cosgrove provided the resources. He assured that no door at Cleveland Clinic would be closed to this book's two photographers—beginning with his own operating room. By way of guidance, Dr. Cosgrove offered a single directive: "Capture the heroism."

Heroic.

Fortunately, there is no shortage of heroism in healthcare. Physicians, nurses, and those who support them take responsibility for human life at its most fragile and vulnerable. Patients and families do what they must to confront difficult diseases and challenging treatments. All stand toe-to-toe with the ultimate foe—mortality—in its thousand different guises.

In healthcare, heroism is supported by another quality: faith. George Crile Jr., M.D., Chairman of General Surgery from 1957 to 1968 and son of Cleveland Clinic founder George Crile Sr., M.D., wrote:

No physician, sleepless and worried about a patient, can return to the hospital in the midnight hours without feeling the importance of his faith. The dim corridor is silent; the doors are closed. At the end of the corridor in the glow of the desk lamp, the nurse watches over those who sleep or lie lonely and wait behind closed doors. No physician entering the hospital in these quiet hours can help feeling that the medical institution of which he is part is in essence religious, that it is built on trust. No physician can fail to be proud that he is part of his patient's faith.

Place.

The doors. The corridor. The glow of the desk lamp. In the quote above, Dr. Crile feels a strong sense of place. He is aware that the rooms and hallways of Cleveland Clinic bear meanings that transcend their physical uses. These buildings are rich with memory, solemn with purpose and potent with hopes and expectations.

Cleveland Clinic's original structures still stand as testament to a mighty heritage of achievement. Here are the sites of Cleveland Clinic's historic firsts: the discovery of coronary angiography; the world's first published coronary artery bypass surgery; the world's first successful larynx transplant; the world's first minimally invasive aortic valve replacement. These buildings have witnessed countless battles with disease, and quiet triumphs recorded only in medical records. Life happened here. Babies were born in these rooms. Generations of physicians and nurses enjoyed long and productive careers within these walls.

Today, Cleveland Clinic's new buildings sparkle in the light of dawn. They gleam with promise and geometric confidence. Seen from a distance, the Cleveland Clinic campus resembles an ultra-modern city-within-a-city. At sunset, the windows of the Lerner Research Institute, Cole Eye Institute and Taussig Cancer Center glow with purposeful activity; late at night, solitary figures make their way down the glass-walled bridges and skyways, a reminder that healthcare has no boundaries set in time.

People.

People are the raison d'être of Cleveland Clinic. They are both what it serves and what it serves up. Tens of thousands of people awaken each morning knowing that Cleveland Clinic will be their day's destination. Patients, employees and visitors travel to its campus with differing roles, but with a united goal: healing.

Cleveland Clinic personnel are intently focused on patients and their needs. At the same time, they are closely attuned to one another. As a collaborative enterprise, Cleveland Clinic values communication and collegiality. "Curbside consults" are common as physicians share their expertise for the good of the patient. Researchers and scientists, many of whom also are practicing physicians, rub shoulders with clinicians to bring the latest scientific knowledge and discoveries to the patient-care setting.

Most Cleveland Clinic physicians also are teachers. Their notions and knowledge are kept sharp by the continual questioning of medical students and physicians-in-training. This give-and-take enriches the intellectual content of the medical environment. The wisdom and insight of experienced physicians are continually challenged by new ideas and fresh perspectives. Trainees learn at the elbows of legendary practitioners, where they absorb lifelong habits of excellence.

It is the patient, of course, who is the center of attention. Every activity, every undertaking is for the benefit of the patient. In the words of Dr. Cosgrove, Cleveland Clinic is a "sought-after haven for patients worldwide."

Timeless.

Art, like medicine, is timeless. But some note must be taken of historical context. *Two Views* was photographed as Cleveland Clinic was undergoing one of the most remarkable transformations in its history: the construction of the Sydell and Arnold Miller Family Pavilion and the Glickman Tower. These two buildings are the largest construction project ever undertaken at Cleveland Clinic. Their completion in 2008 will reorient Cleveland Clinic's visual center of gravity and greatly alter the look of its campus and environs.

This book might have waited for Cleveland Clinic to achieve stasis. But, it might have waited forever. For if there is one eternal fact about Cleveland Clinic, it is that it is always expanding, always improving, continually recreating itself to better accomplish its patient care mission, and the research and education that enhance it. Cleveland Clinic has changed, is changing and will continue to change well into the future.

This book, however, uncovers some truths about Cleveland Clinic that will never alter: its dedication to patient care; the commitment of its people; and the energy and compassion with which Cleveland Clinic confronts the challenges of sickness, health, life and humanity.

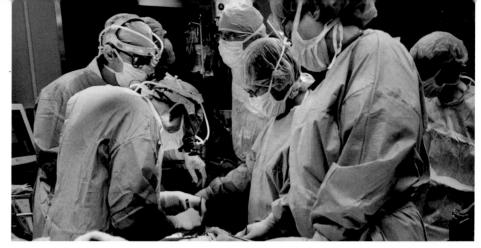

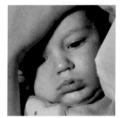

Wherever the
art of medicine
is loved, there
is also a love
of humanity.

HIPPOCRATES

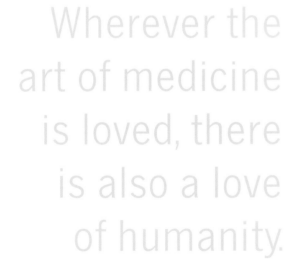

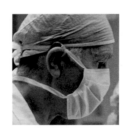

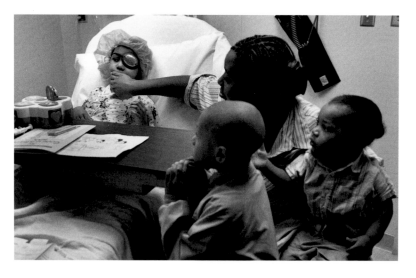

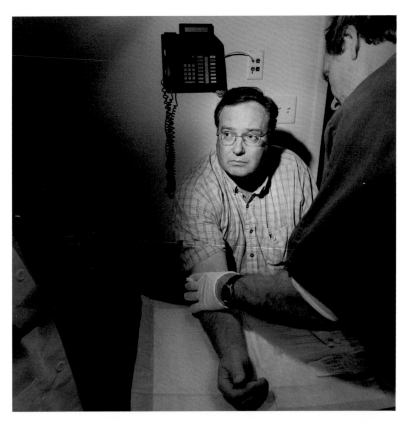

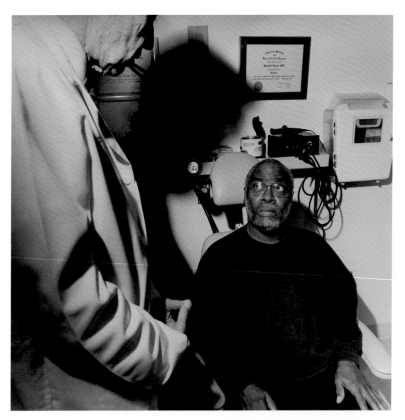

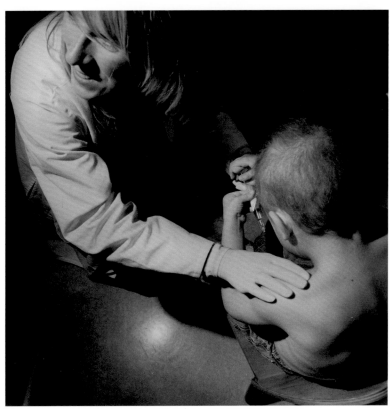

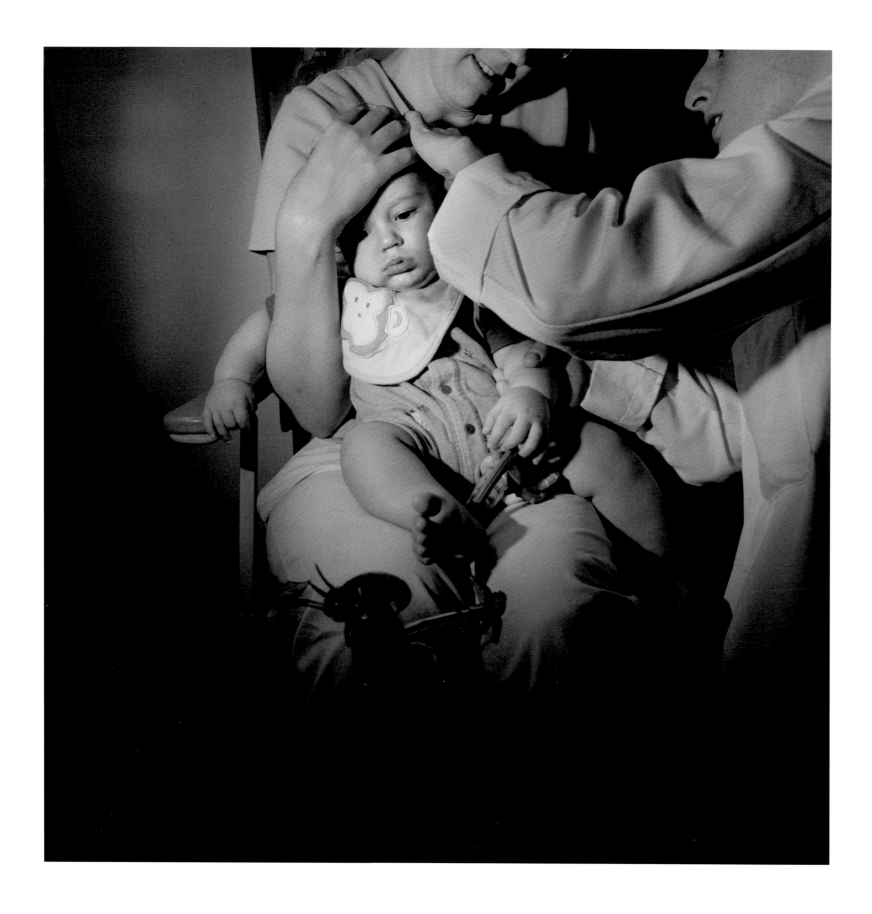

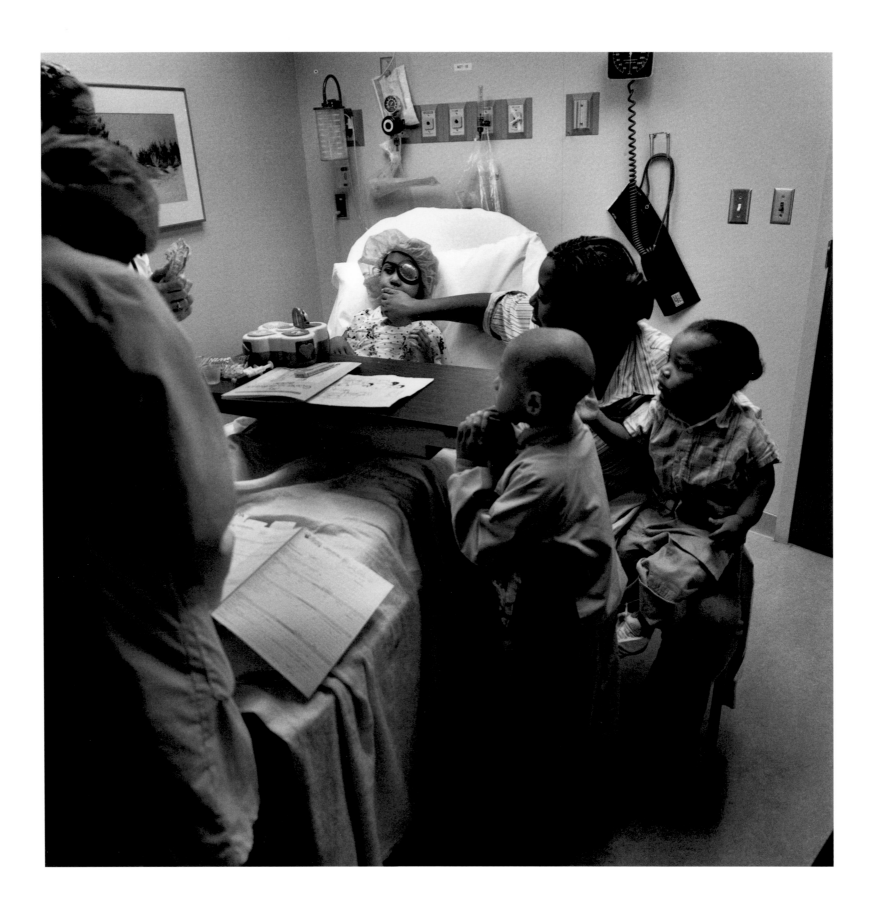

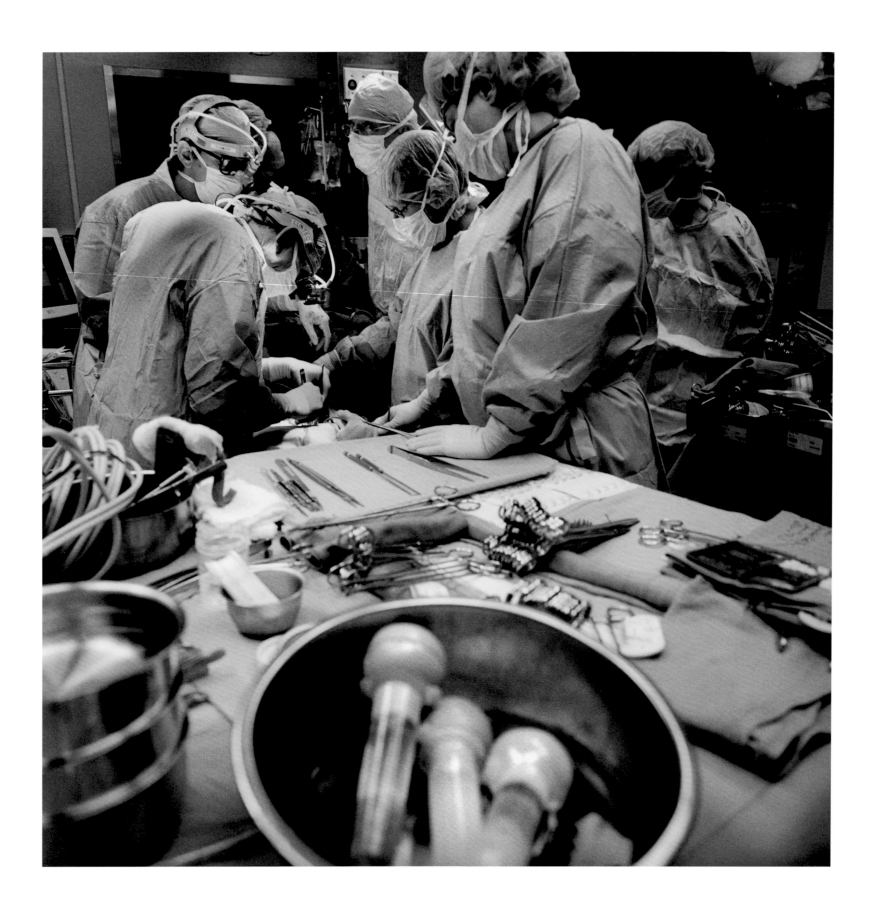

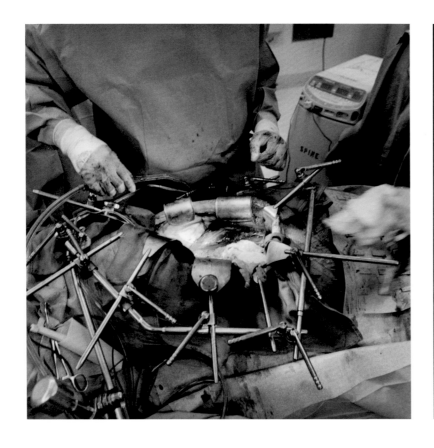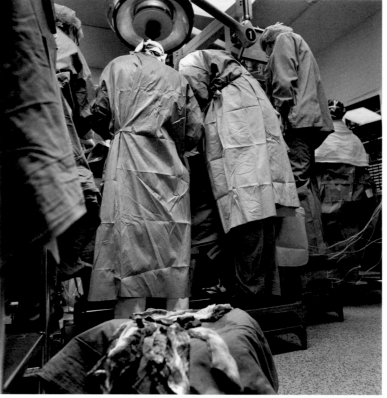

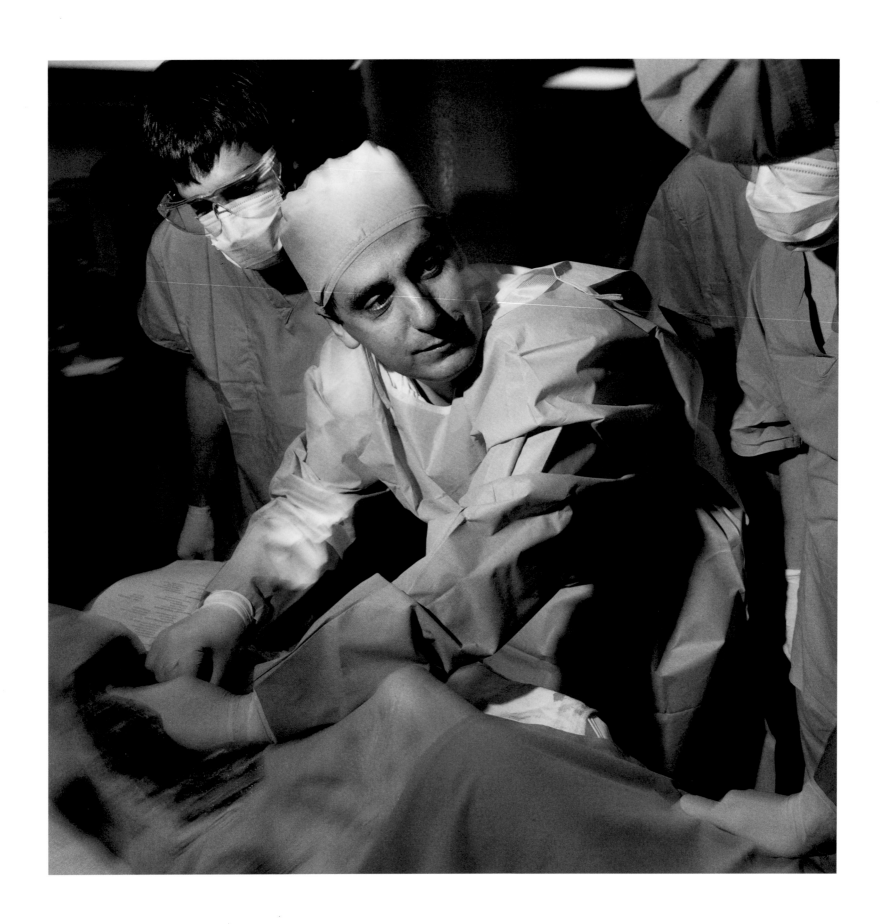

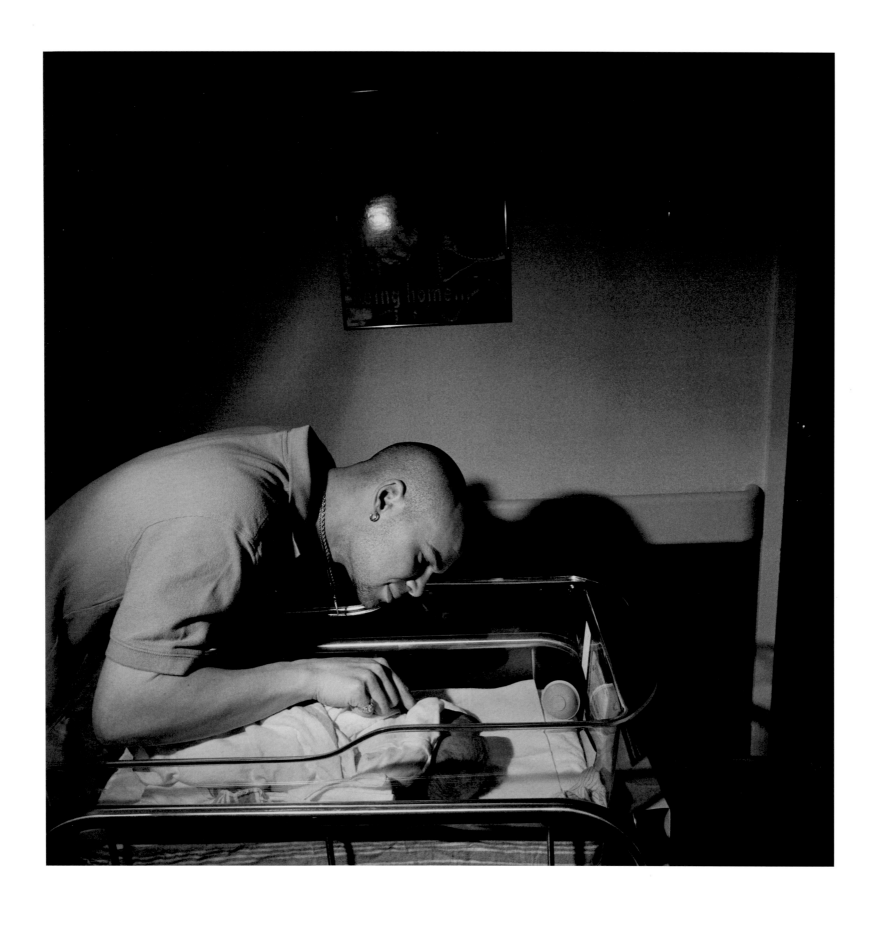

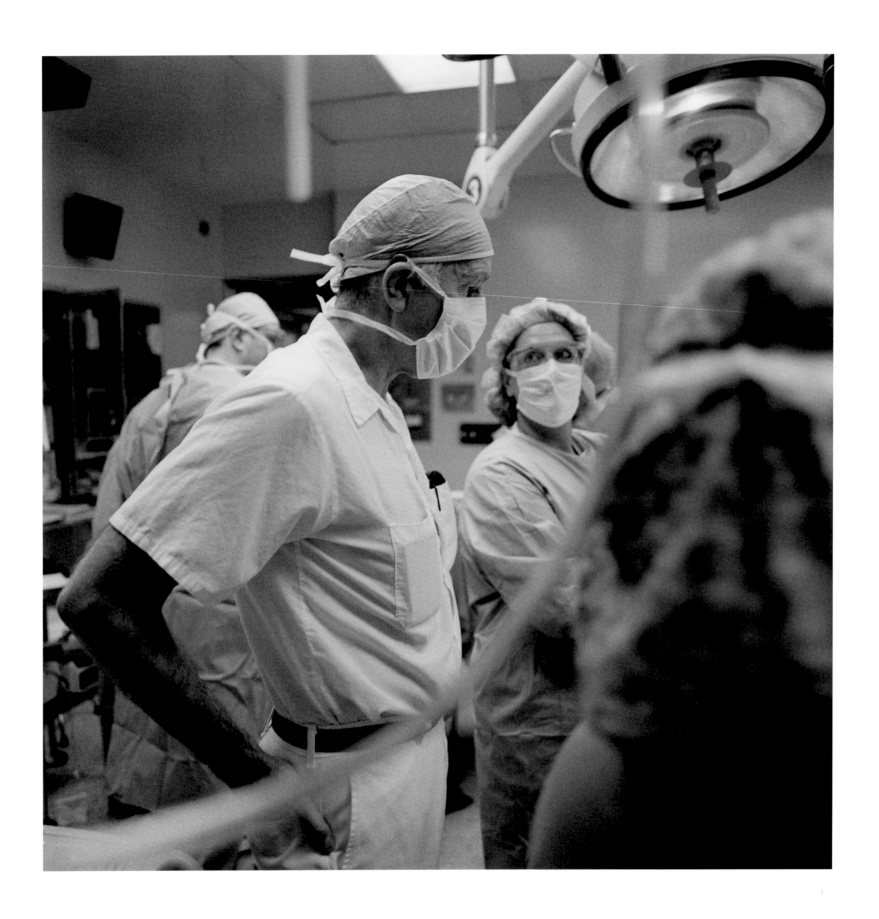

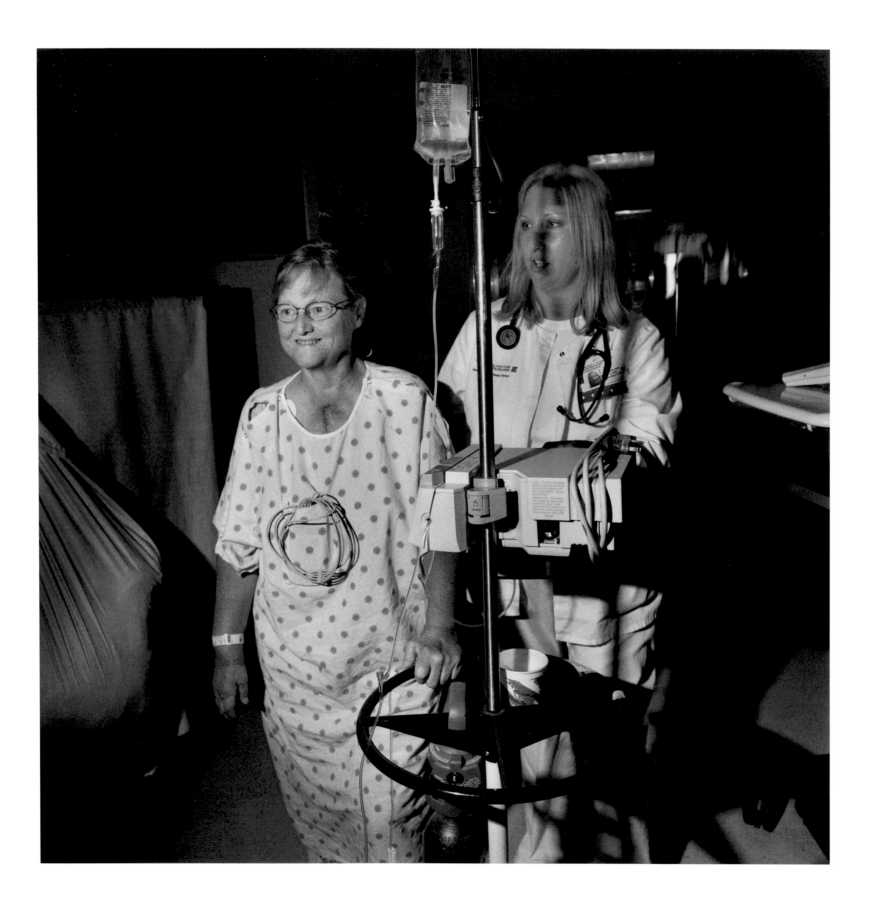

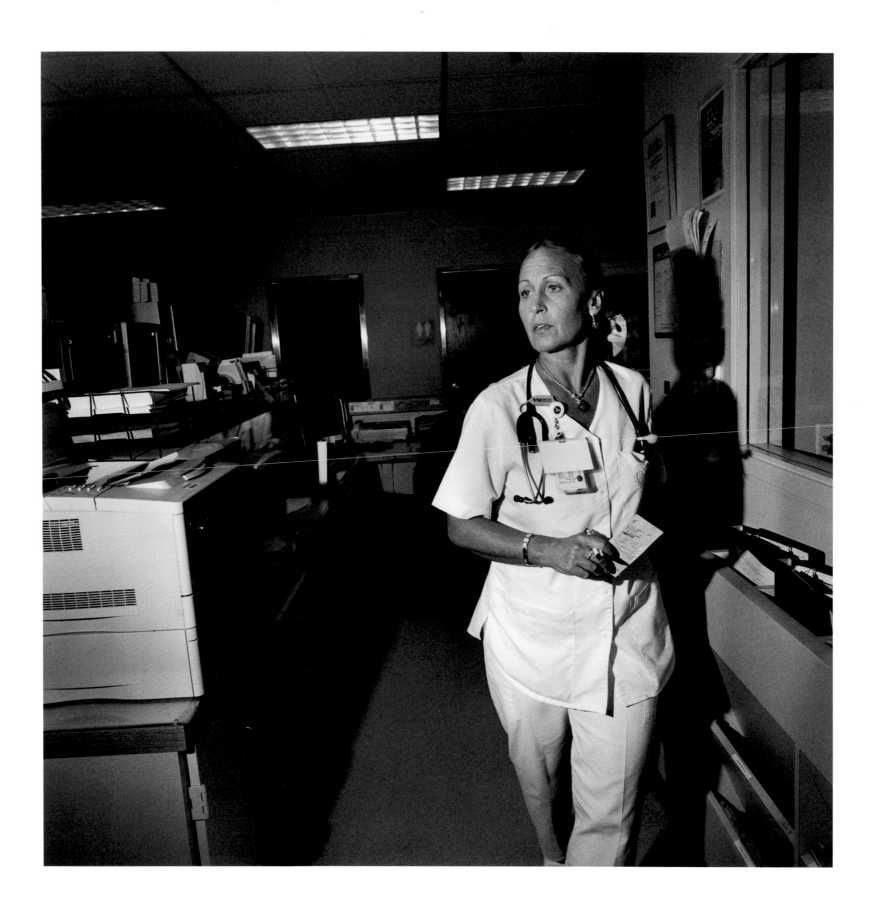

In illness, the
physician is
a parent; in
convalescence,
a friend; when
health is restored,
a guardian.

BRAHMANIC SAYING

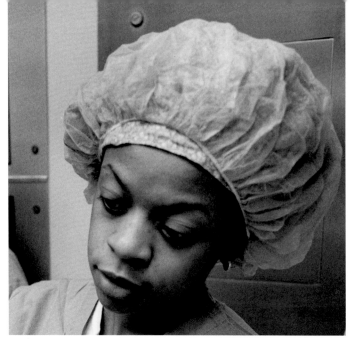

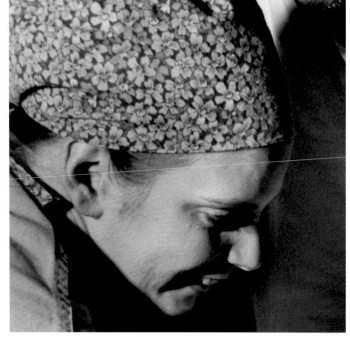

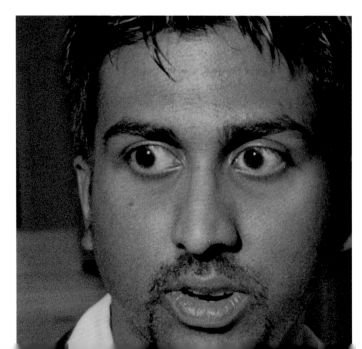

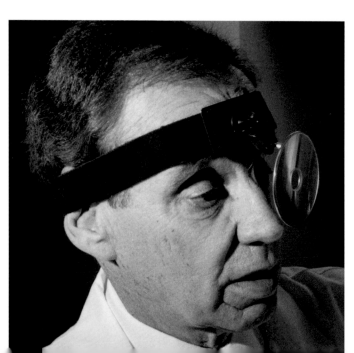

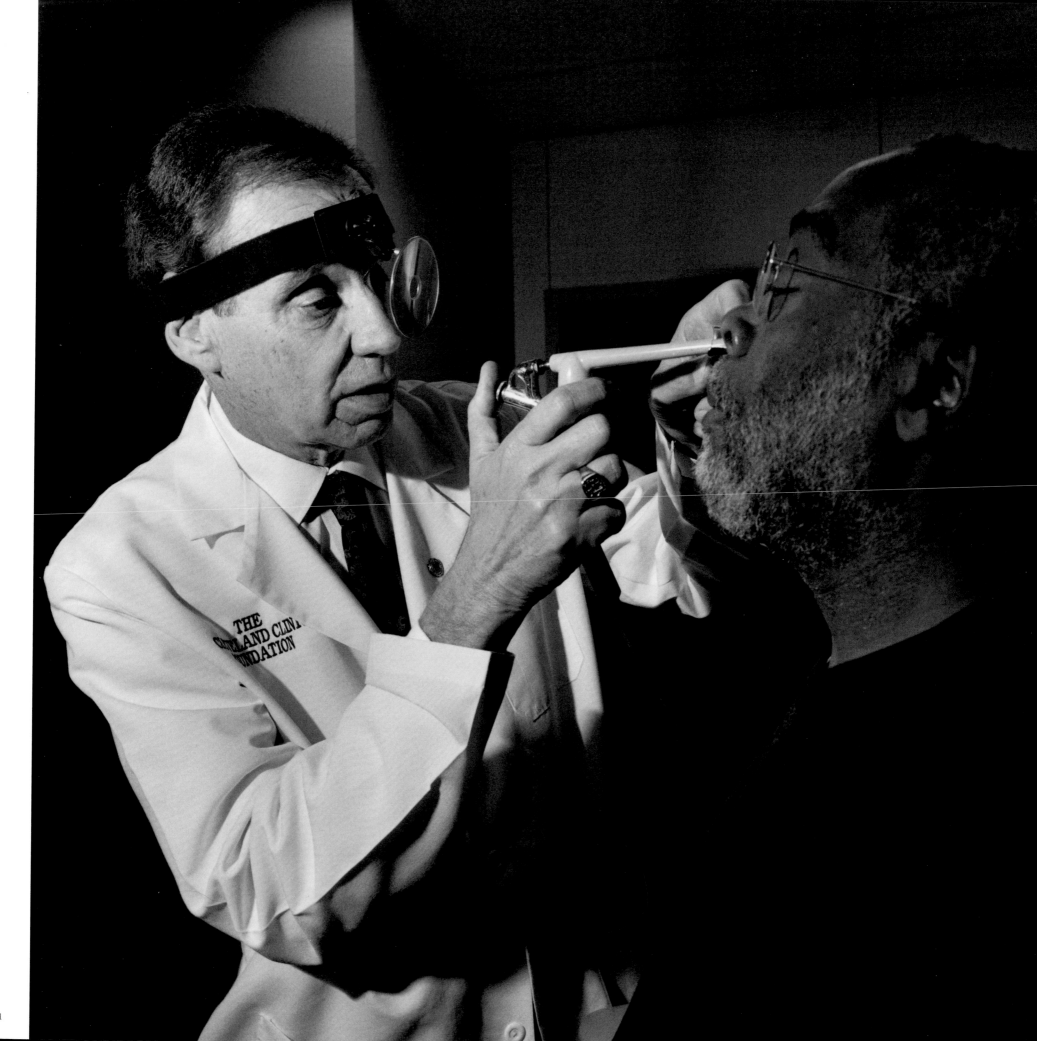

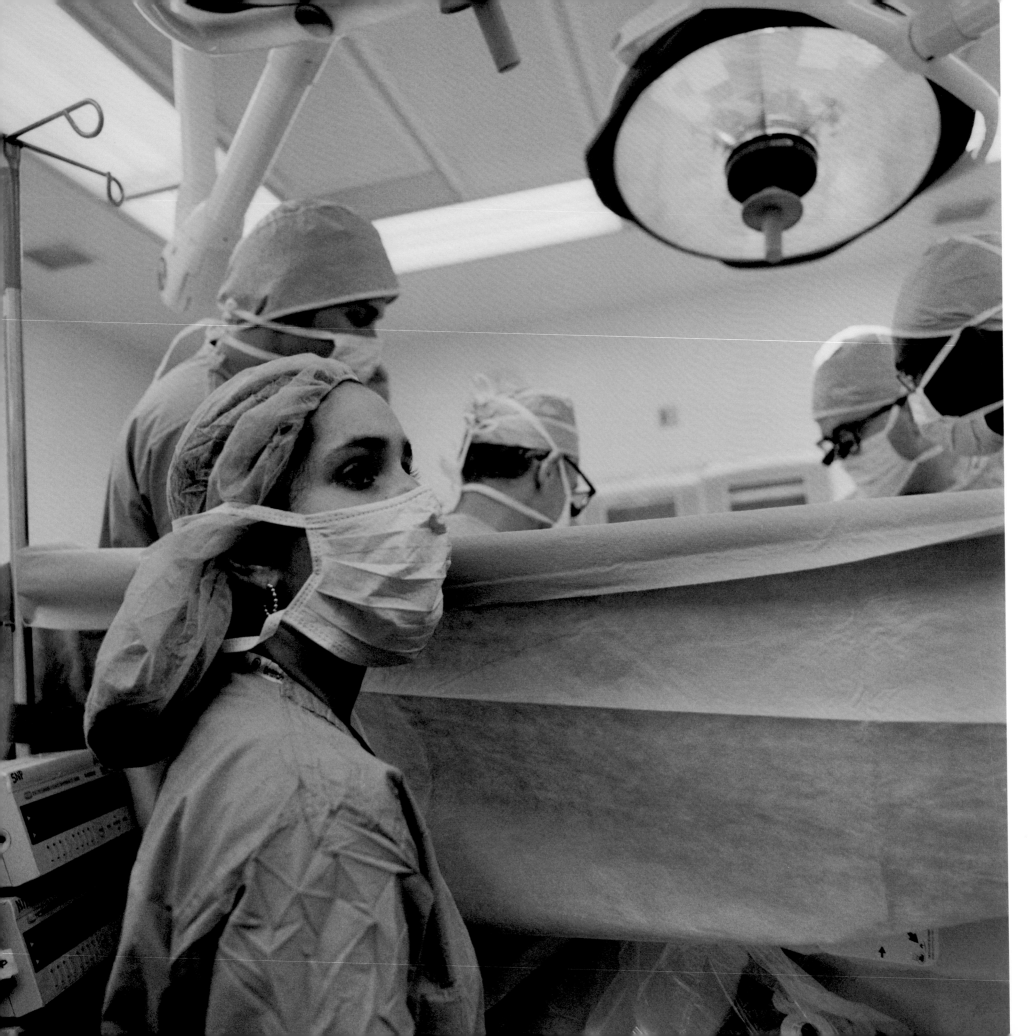

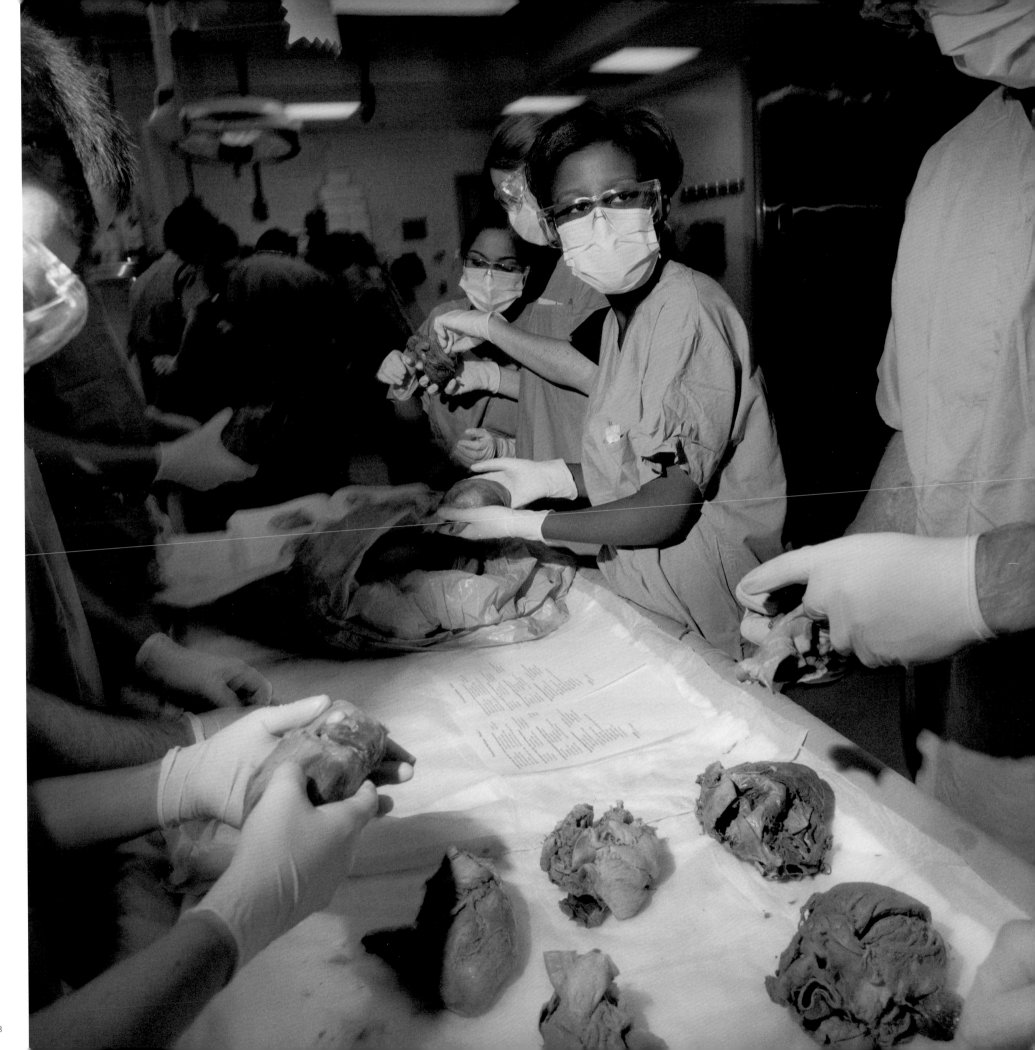

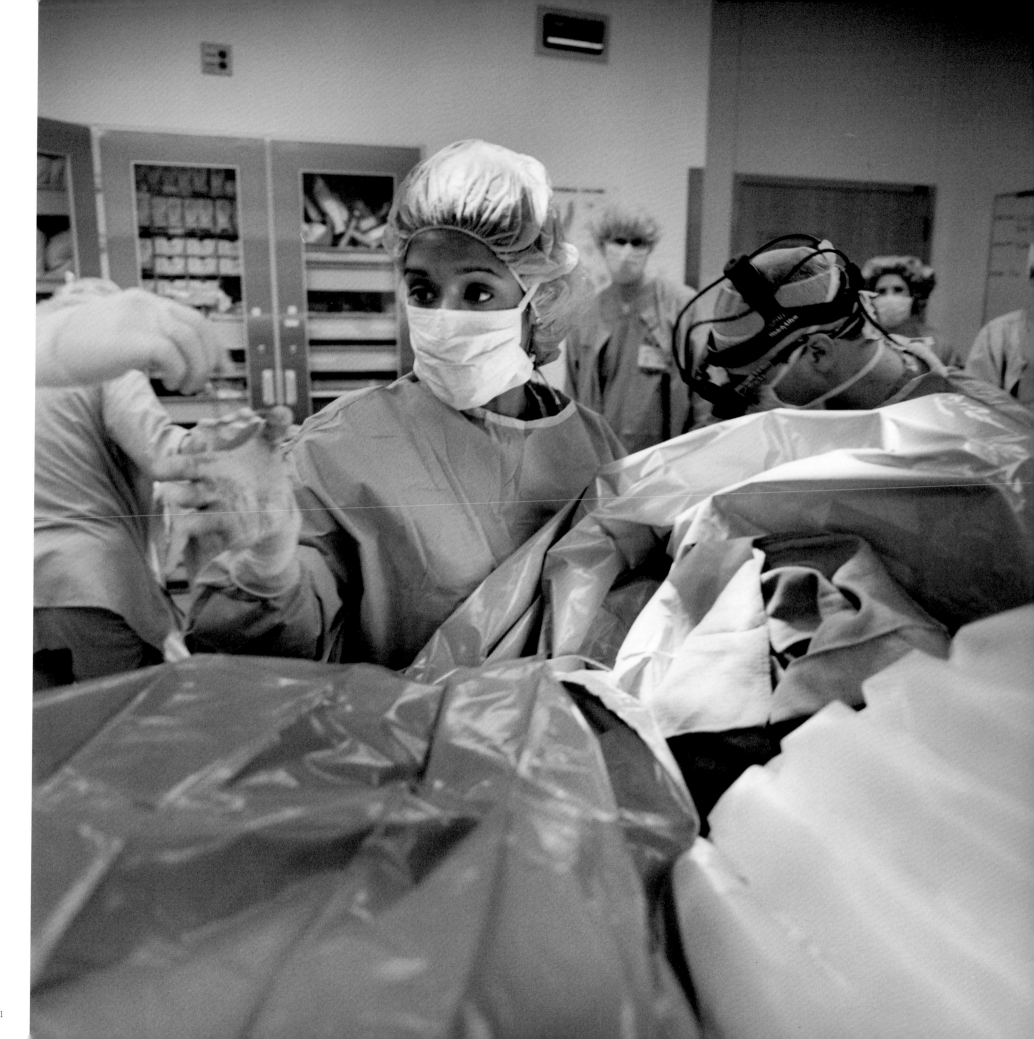

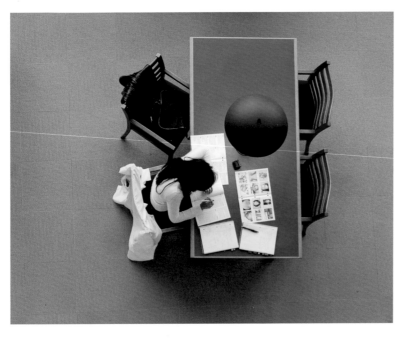

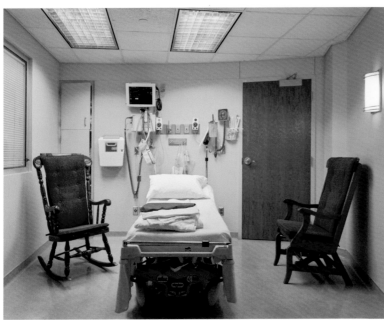

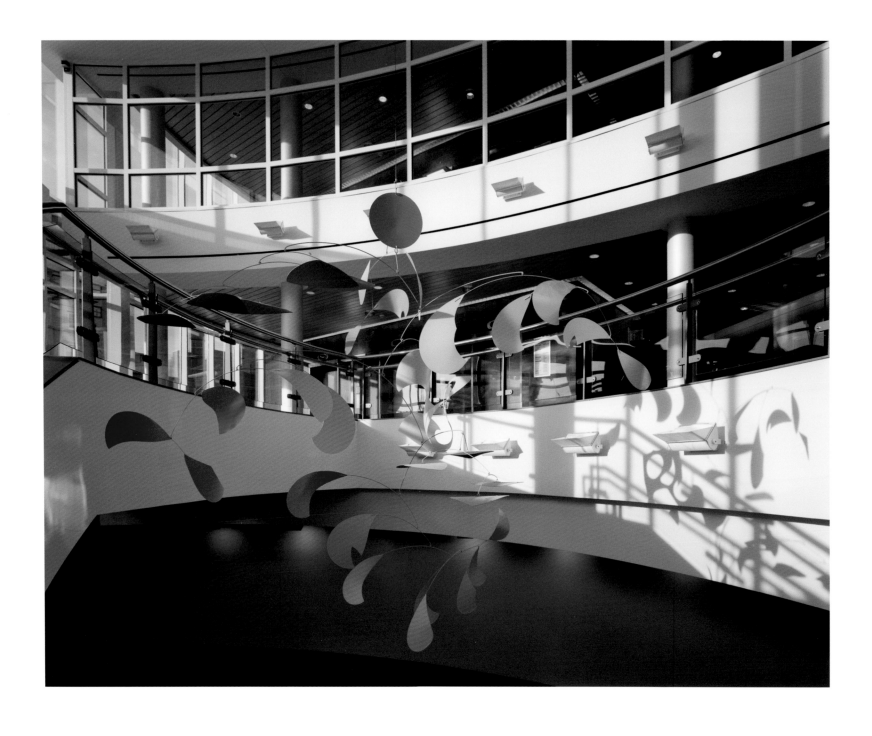

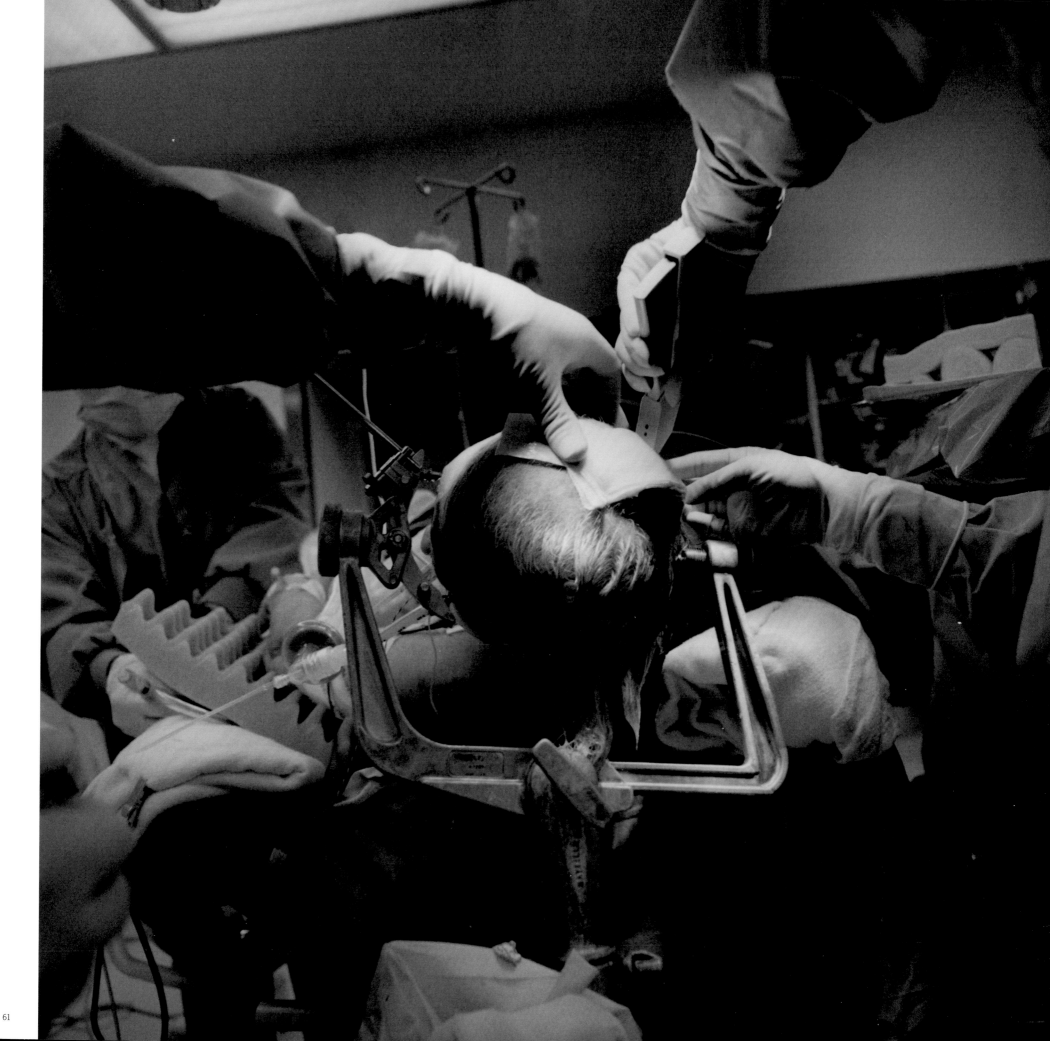

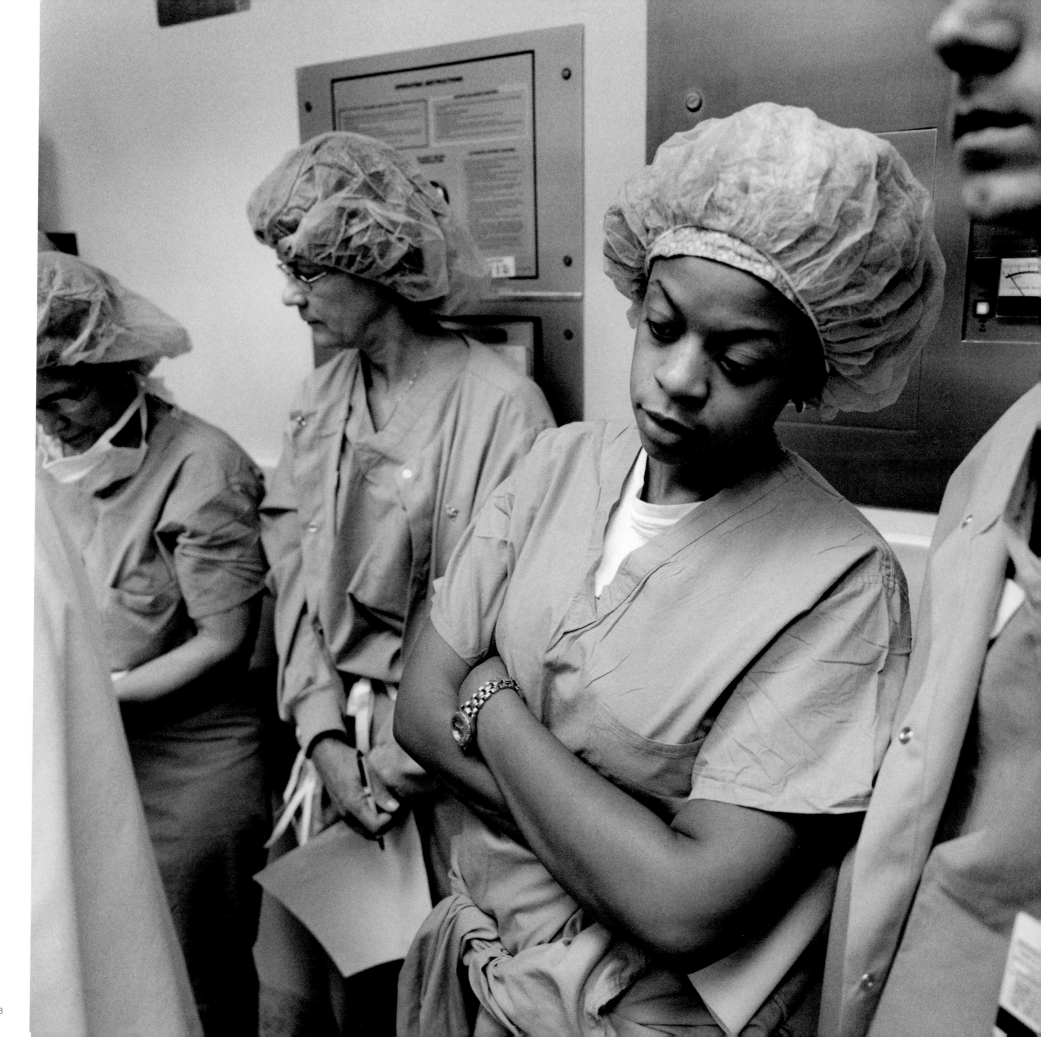

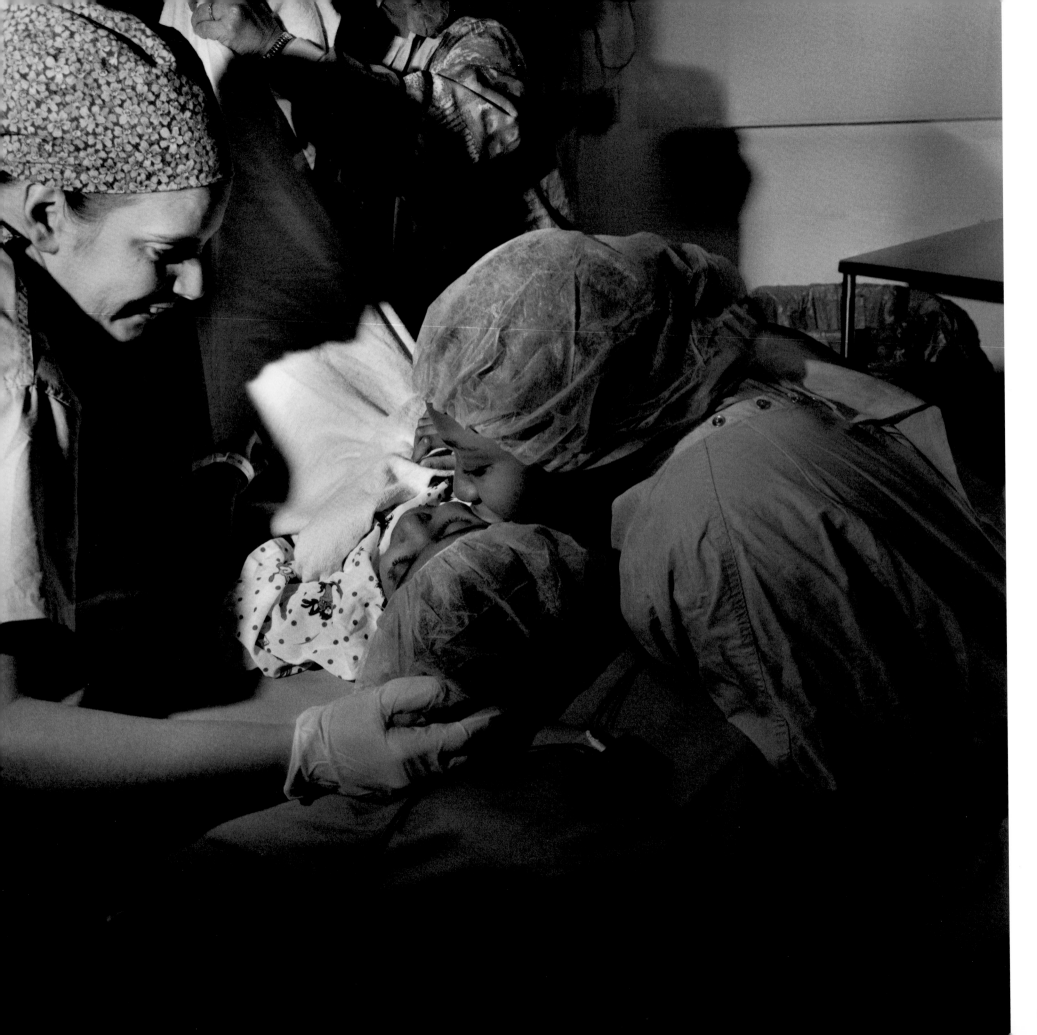

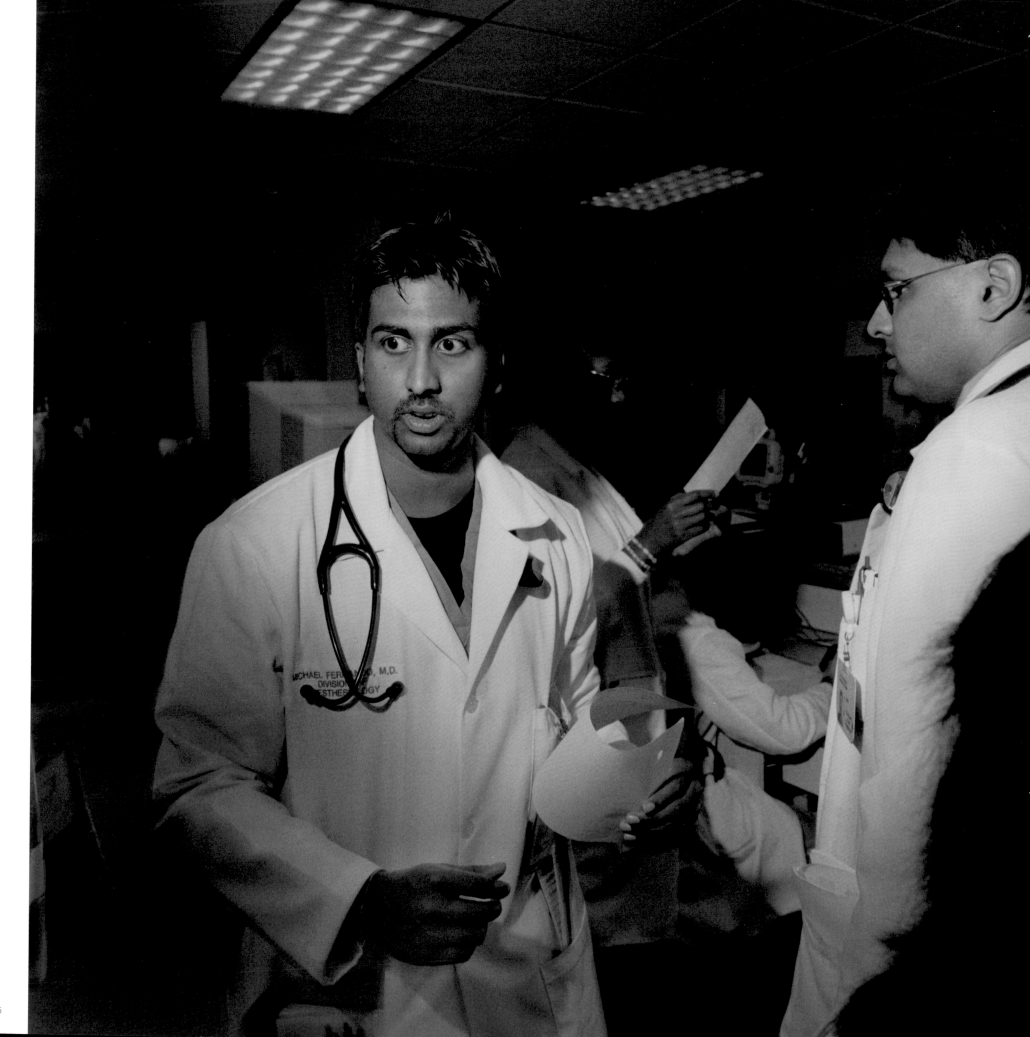

Here, at whatever
hour you come,
you will find light
and help and
human kindness.

ALBERT SCHWEITZER

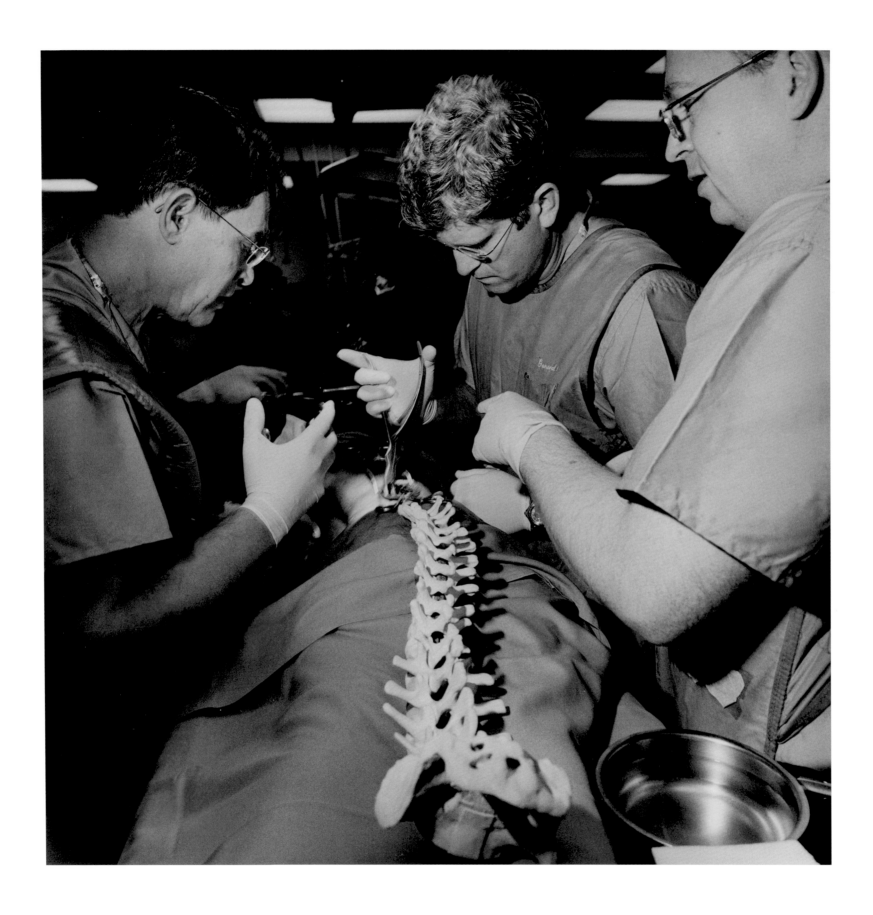

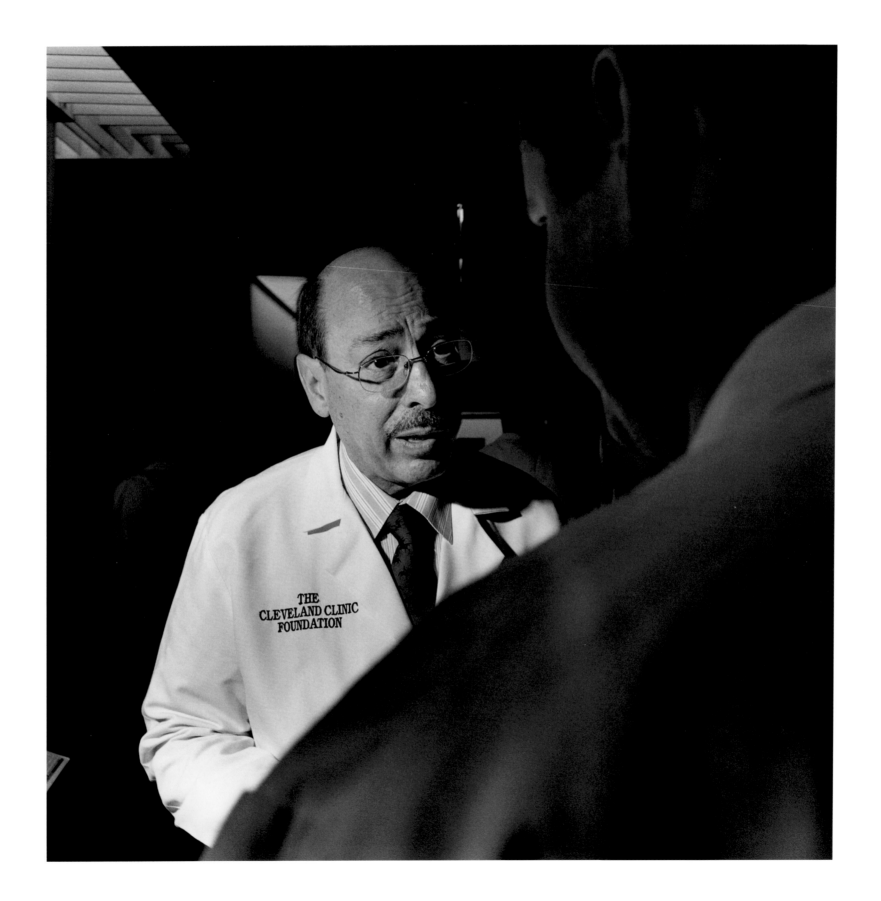

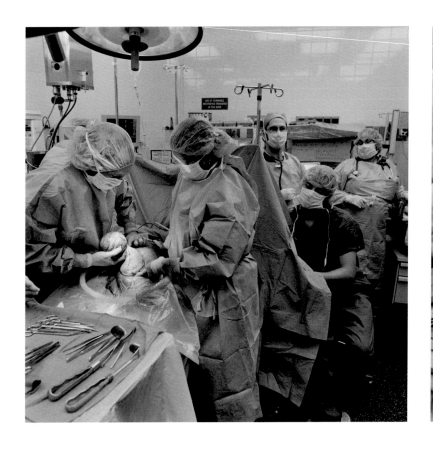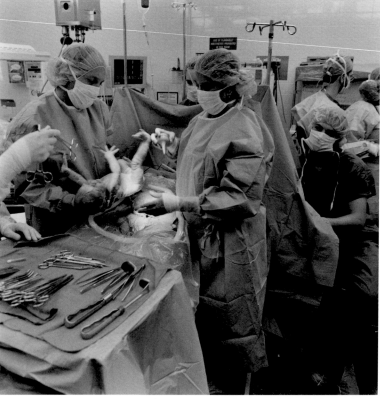

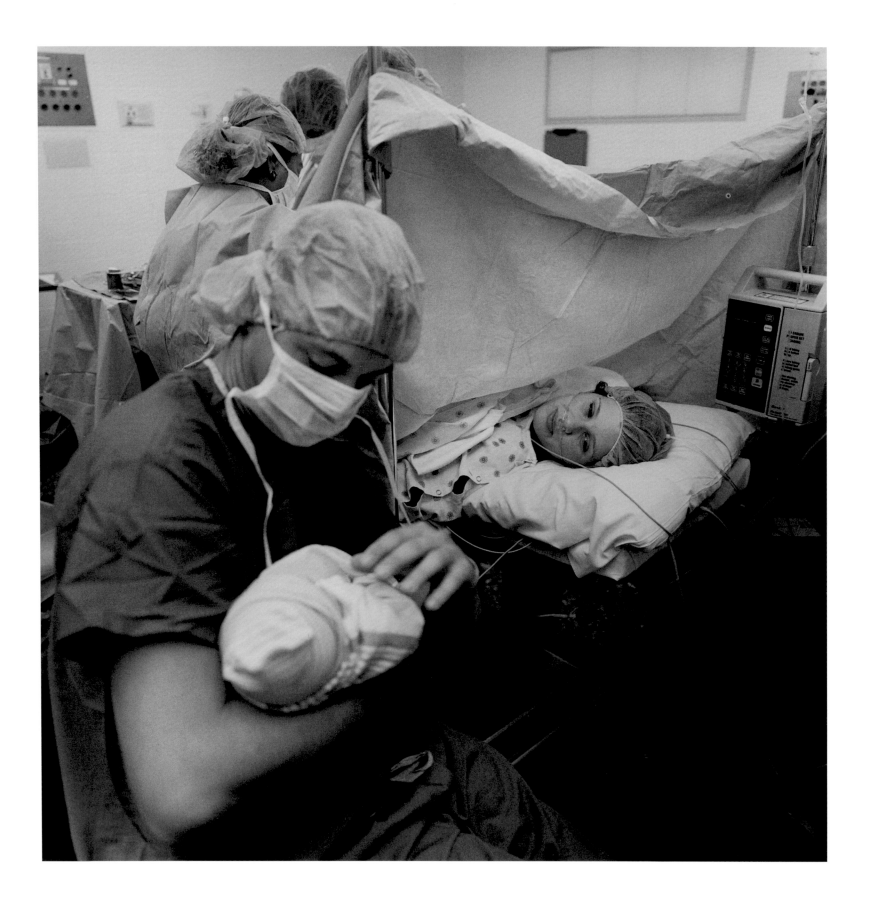

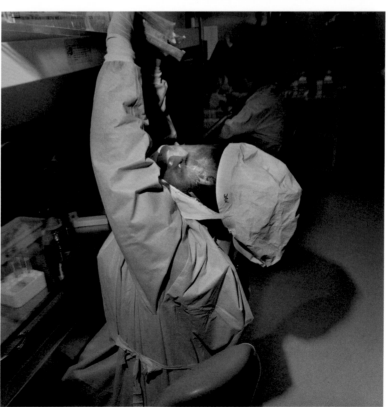

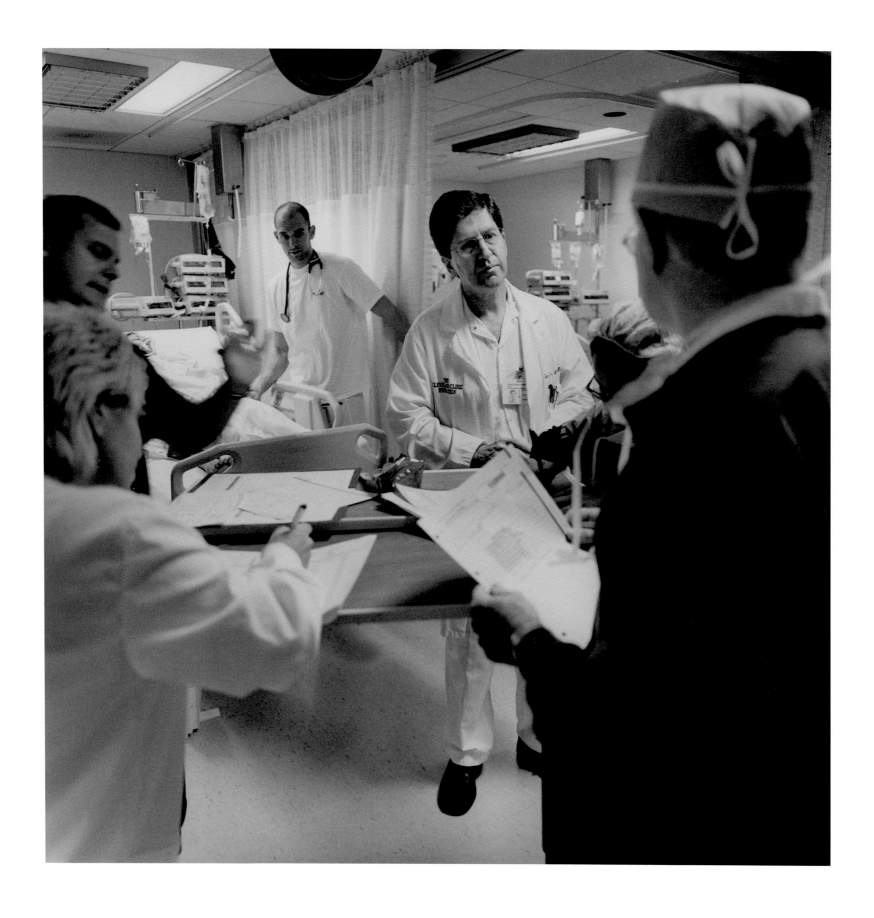

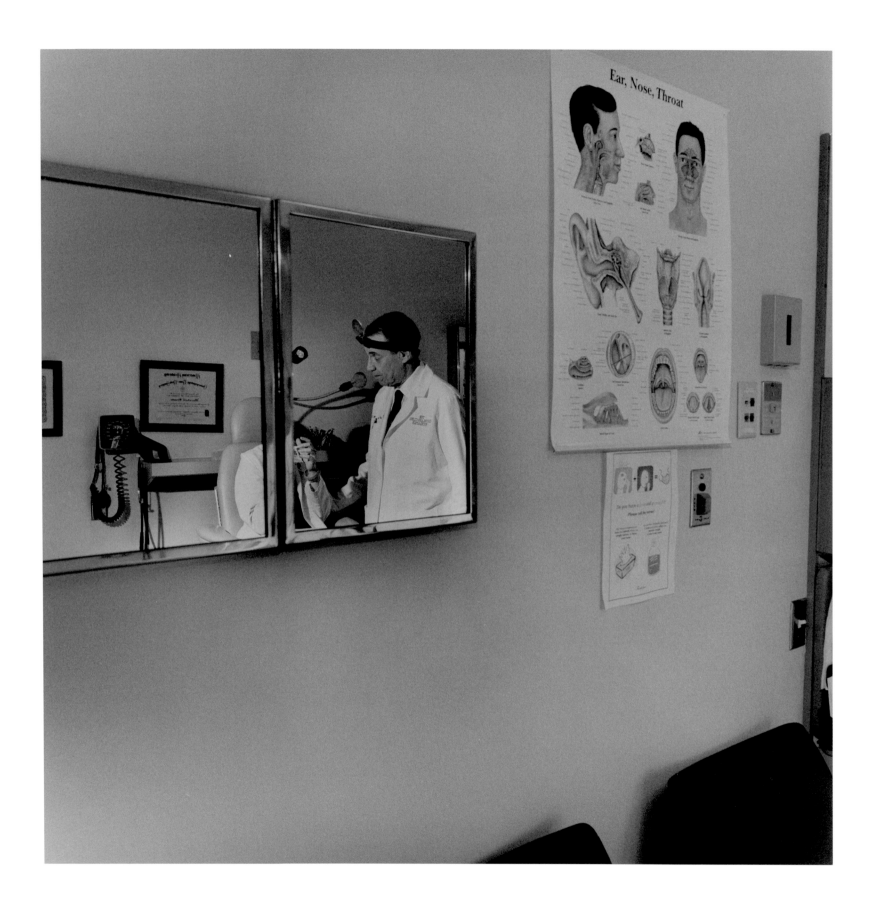

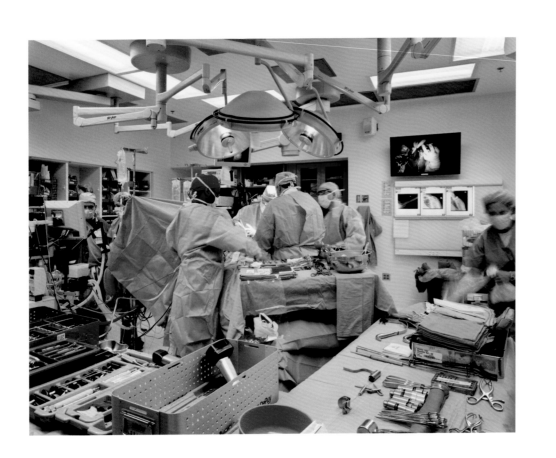

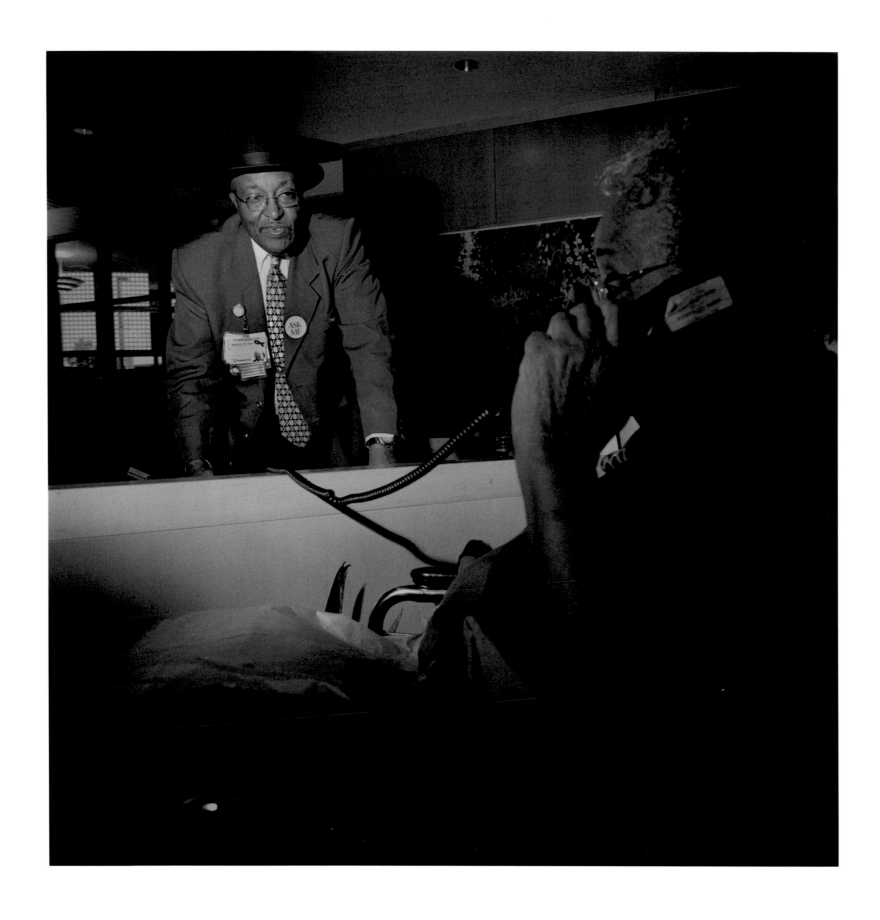

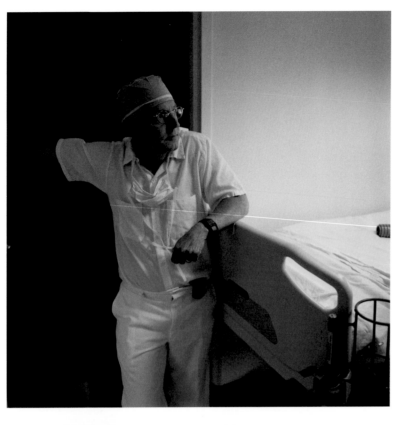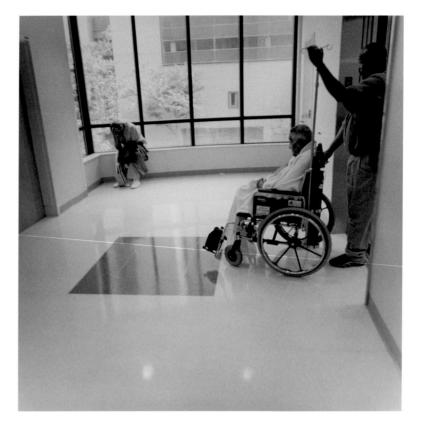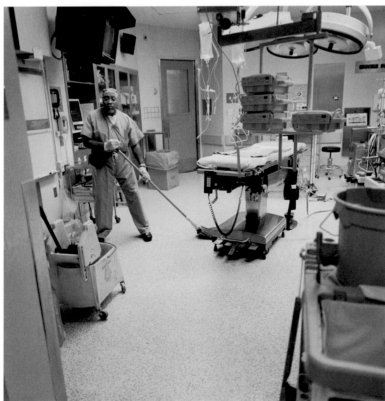

The physician
strives for the
good as the
artist strives for
the beautiful,
each pushed
on by virtue.

HONORÉ DE BALZAC

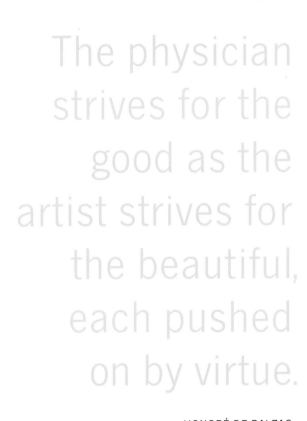

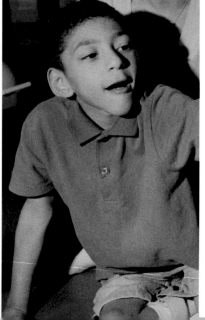

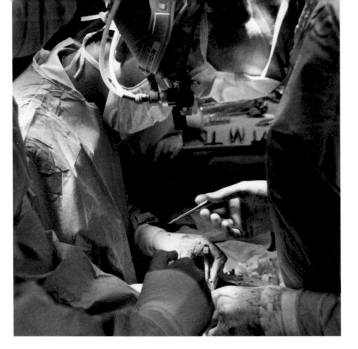

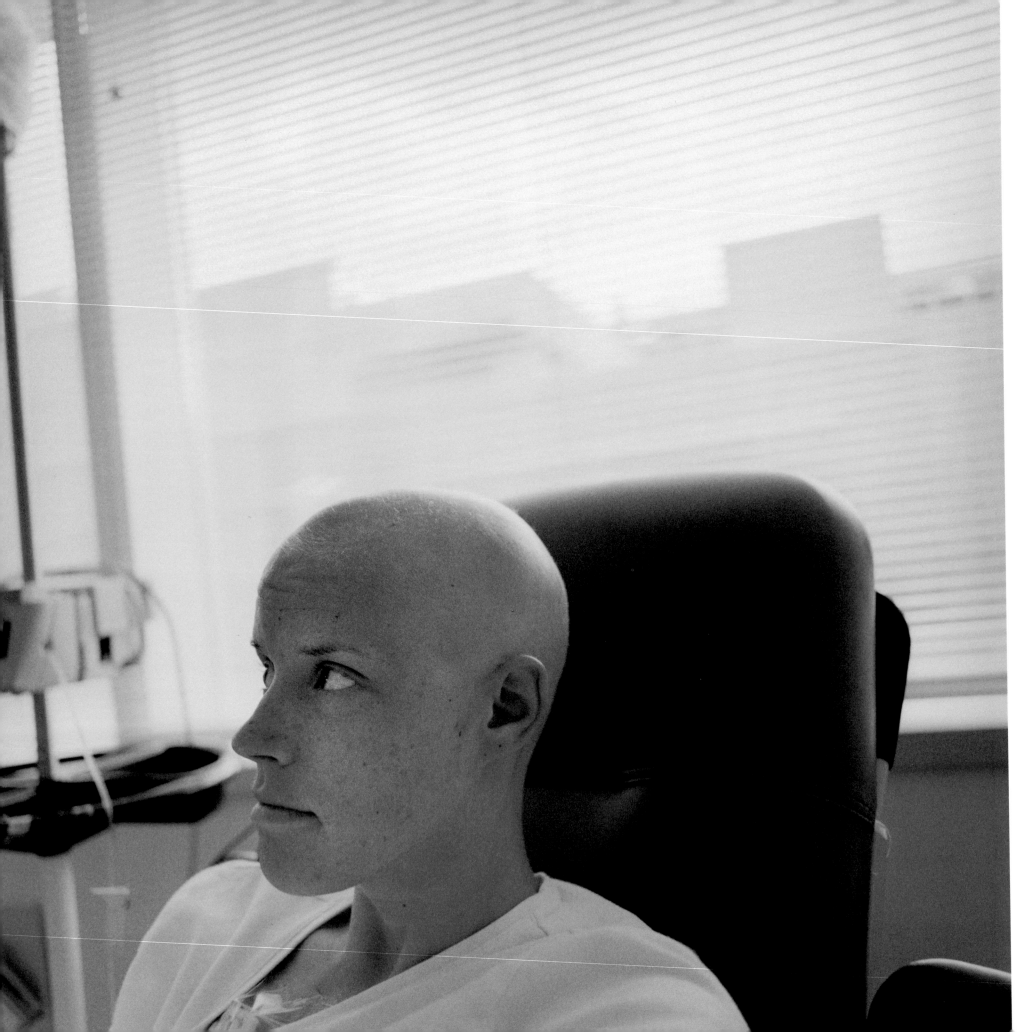

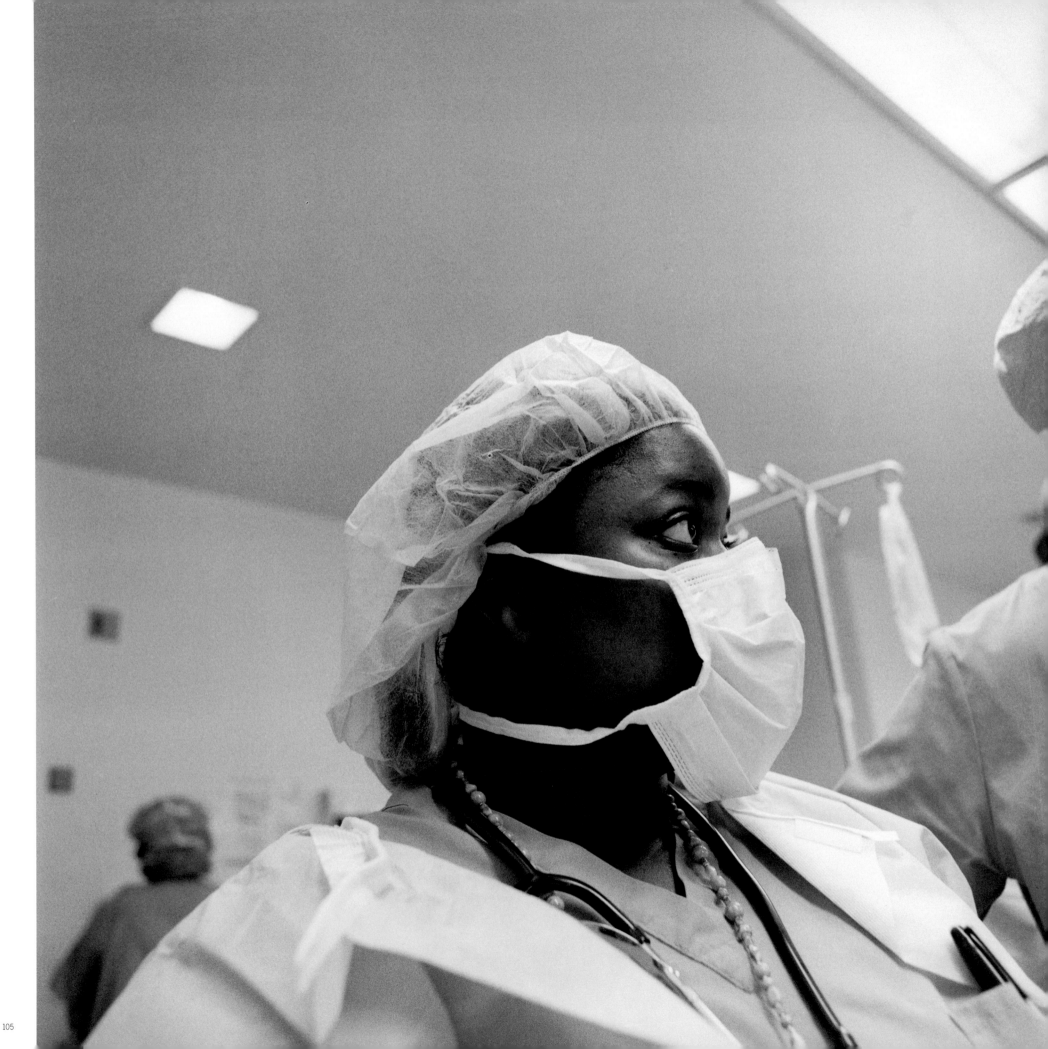

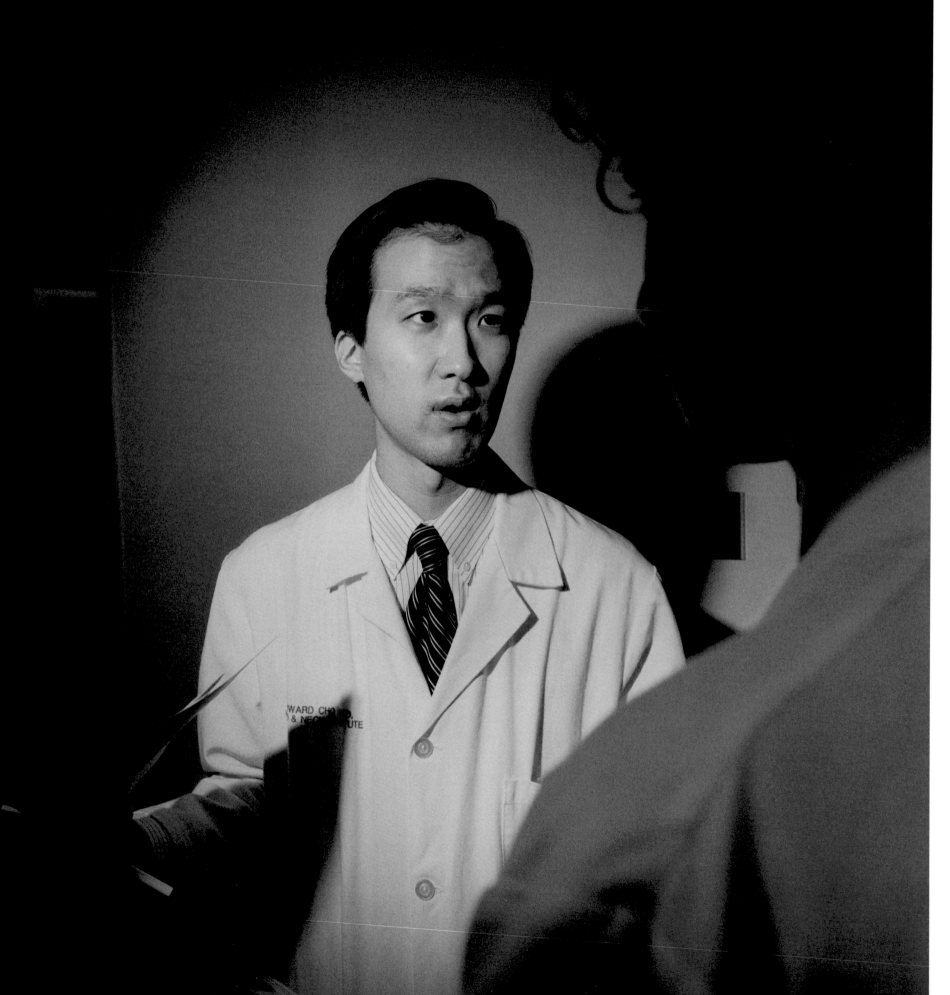

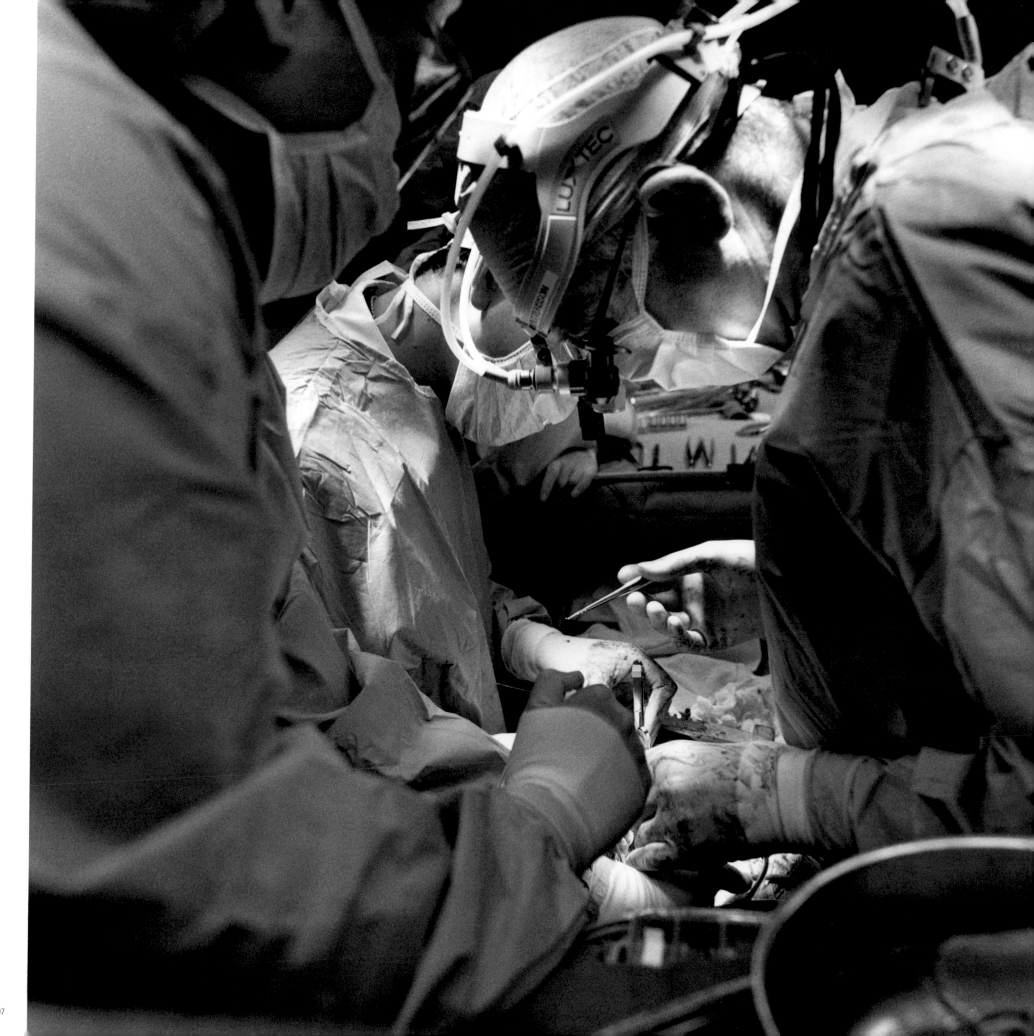

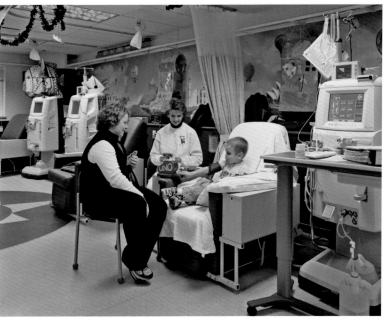

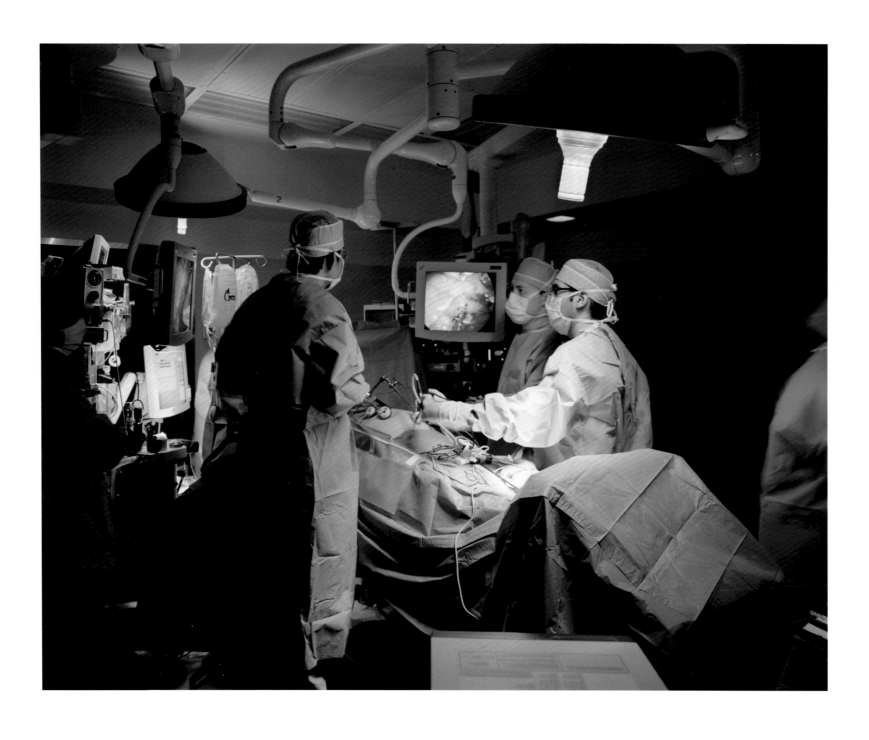

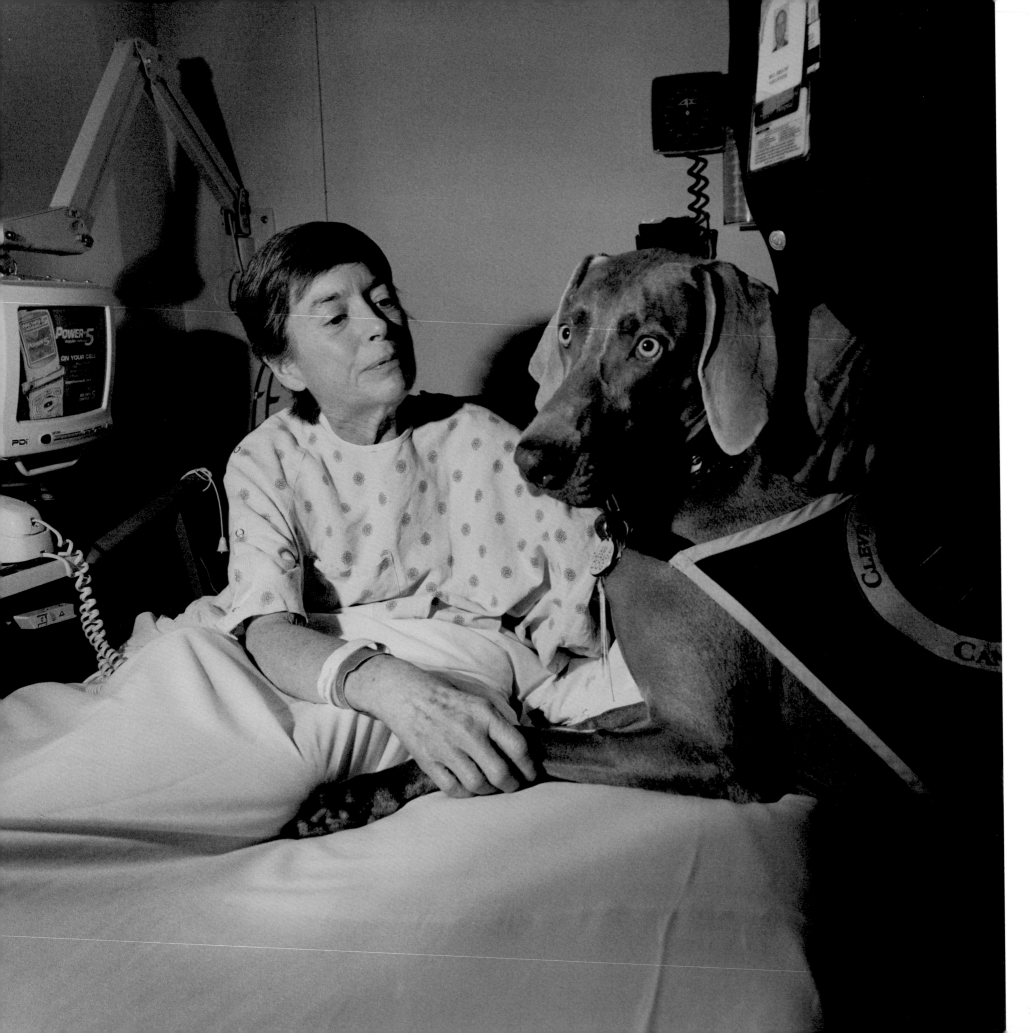

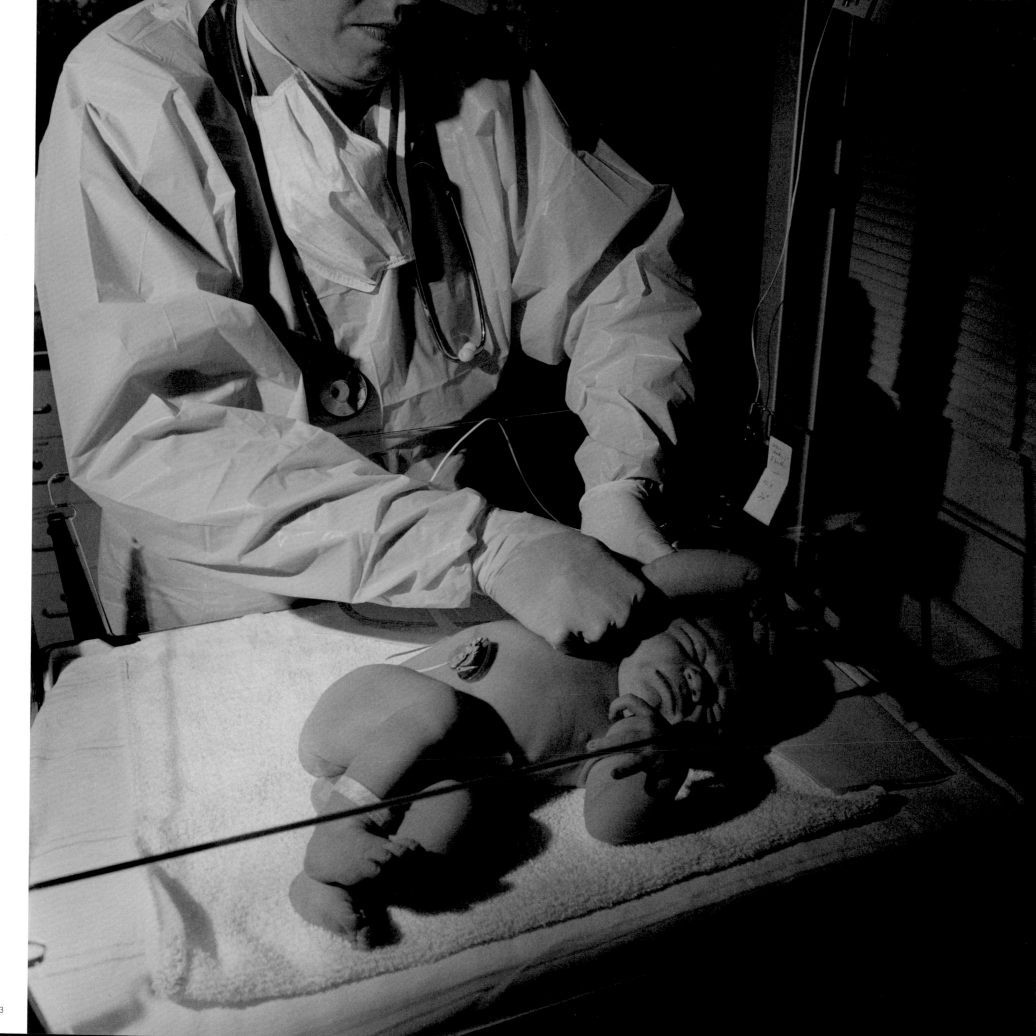

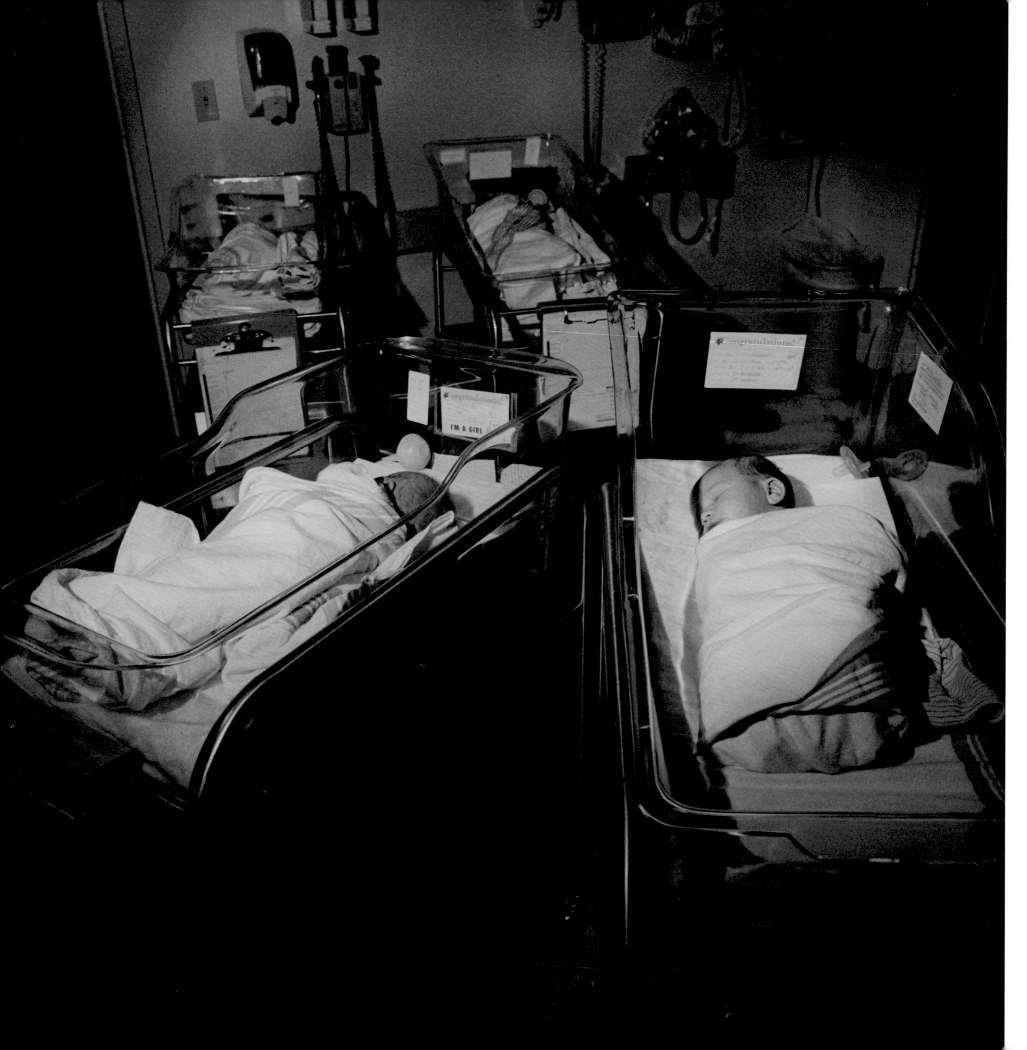

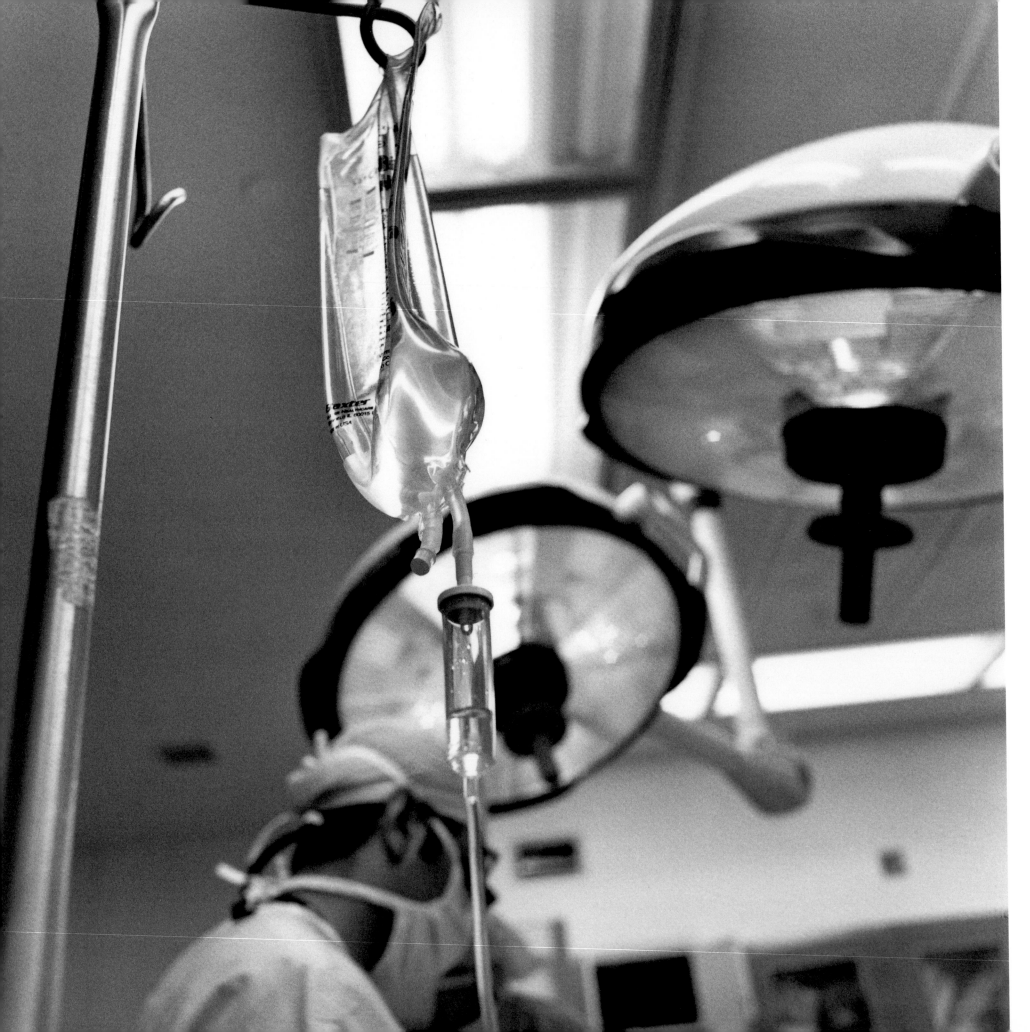

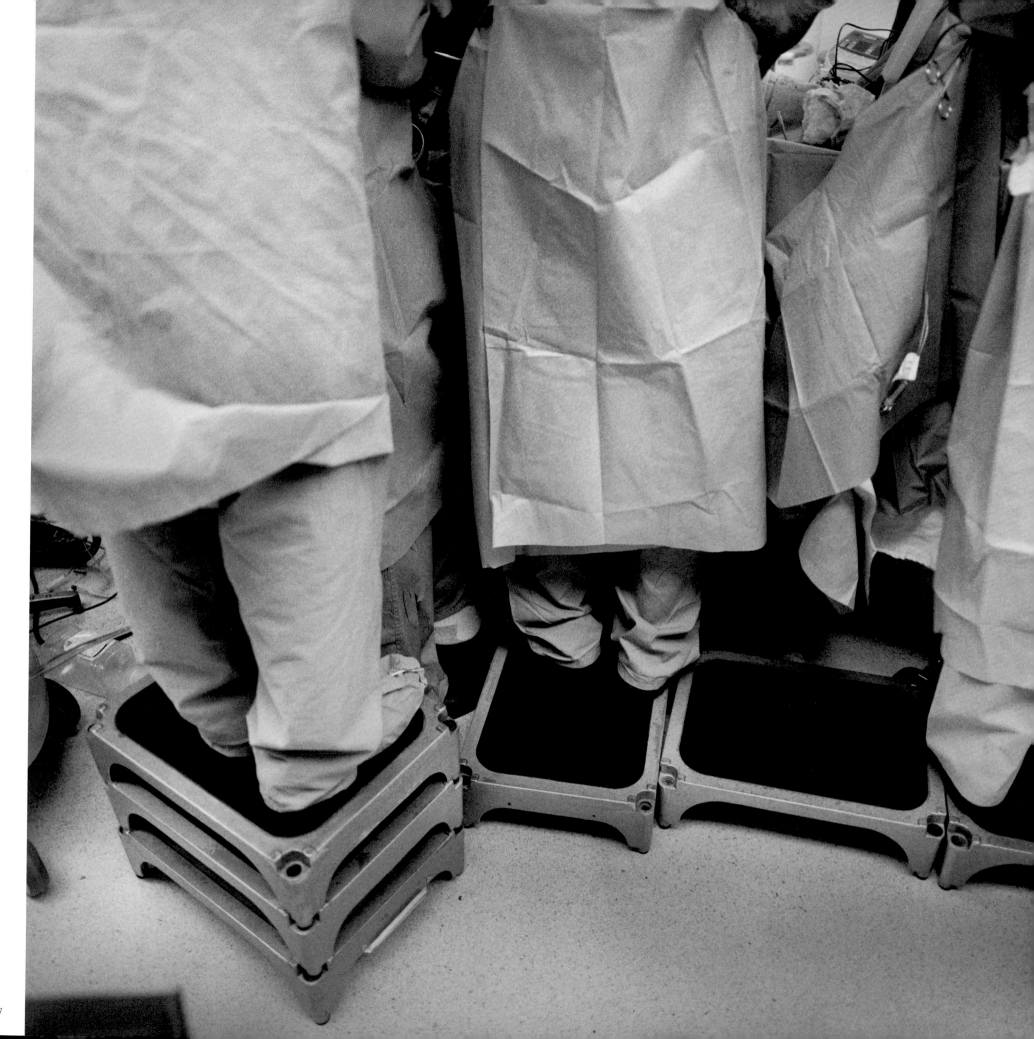

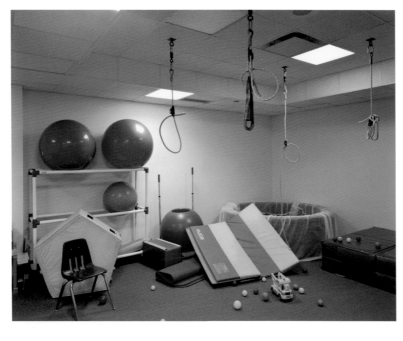

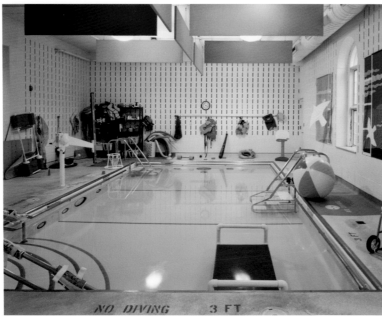

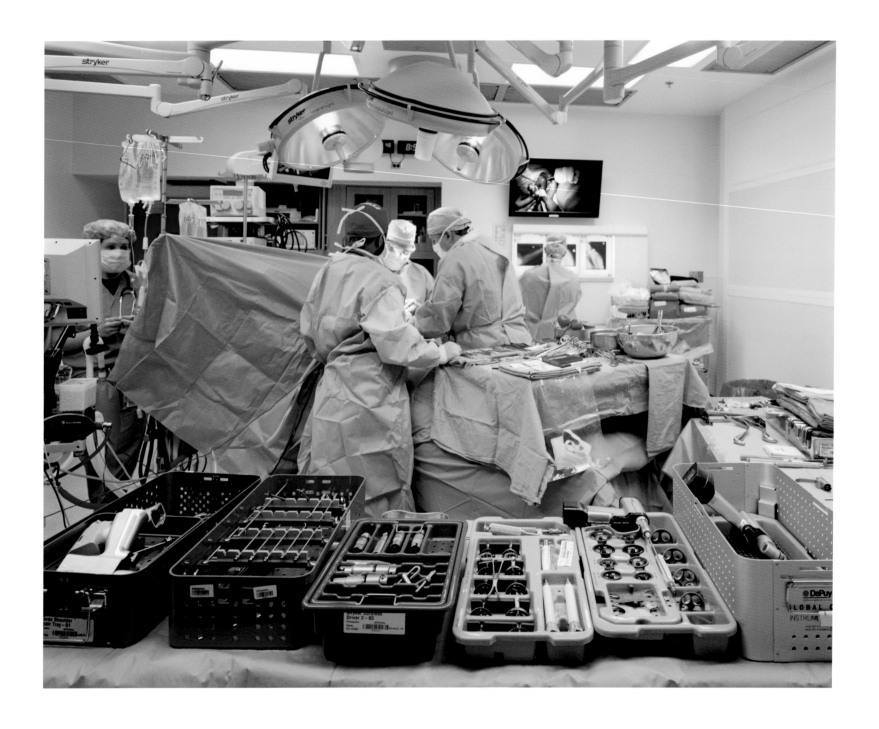

Each of us will accept as our reward... the comfort, and usefulness and prolongation of human life.

GEORGE CRILE SR., M.D.
ONE OF THE FOUR FOUNDERS OF CLEVELAND CLINIC

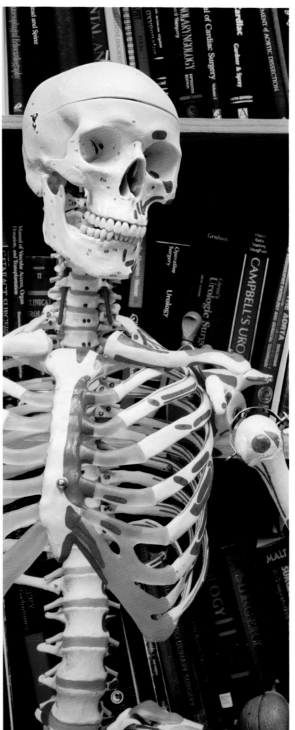

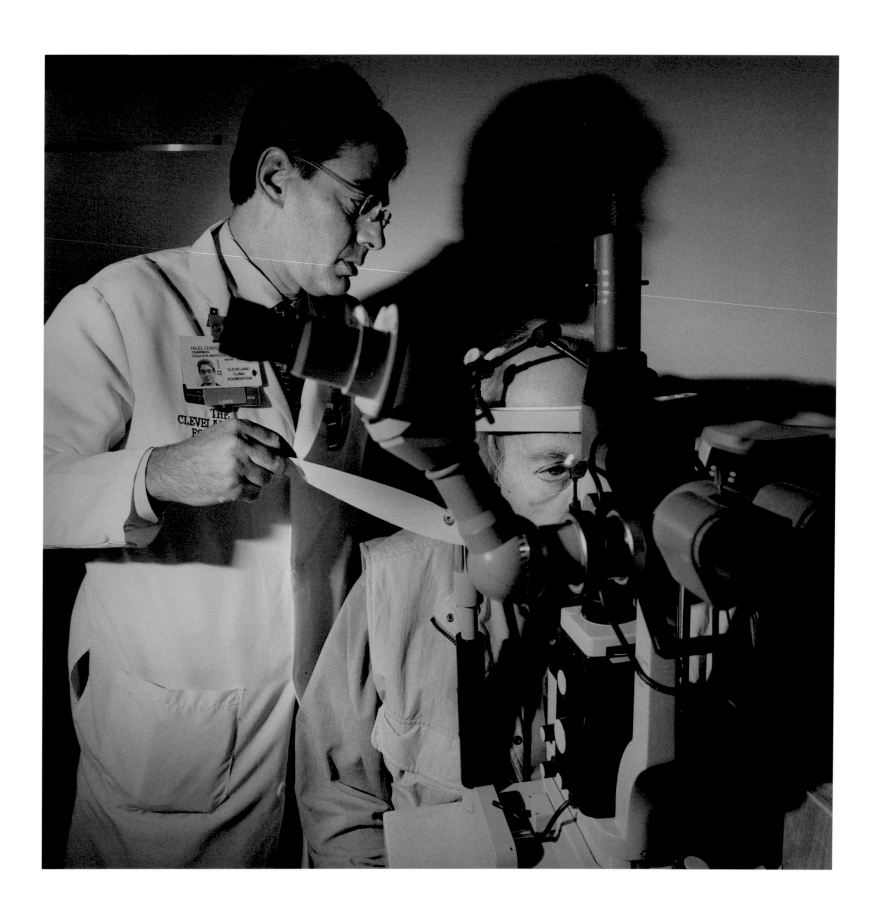

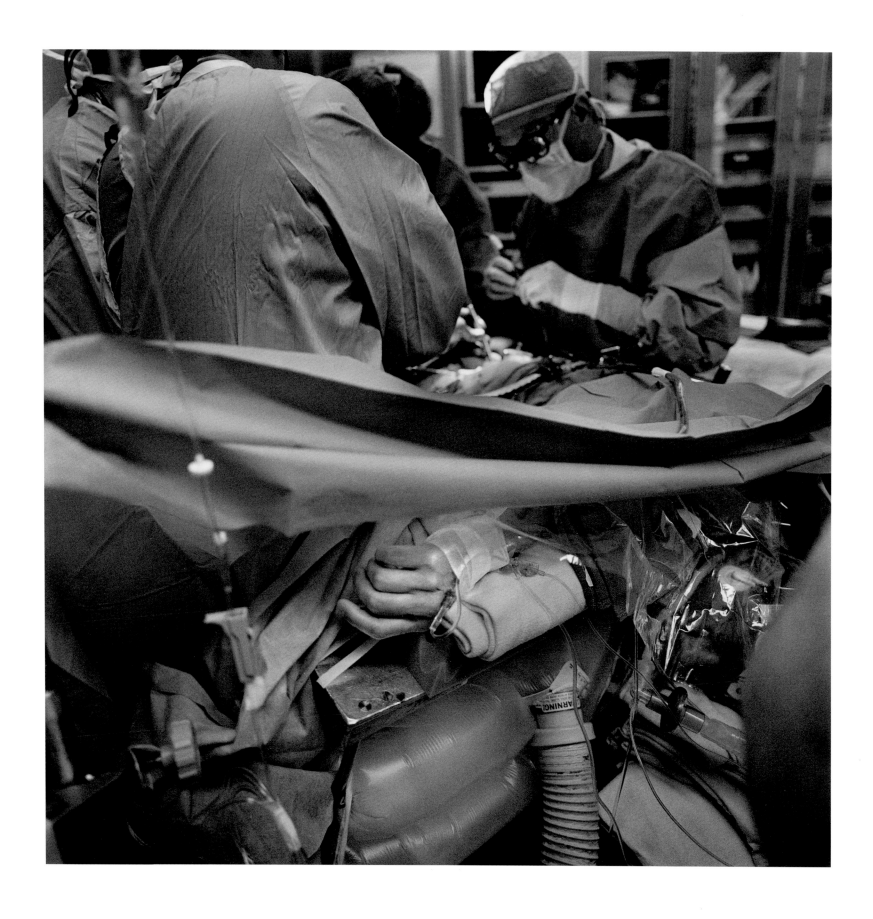

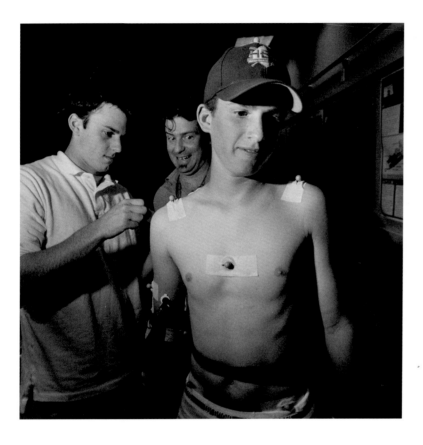 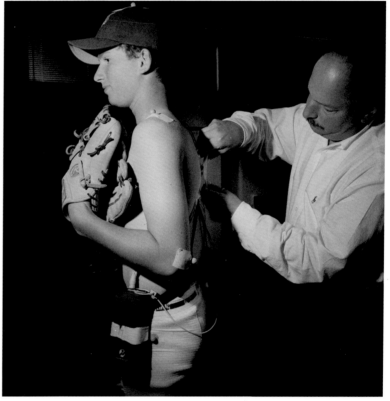

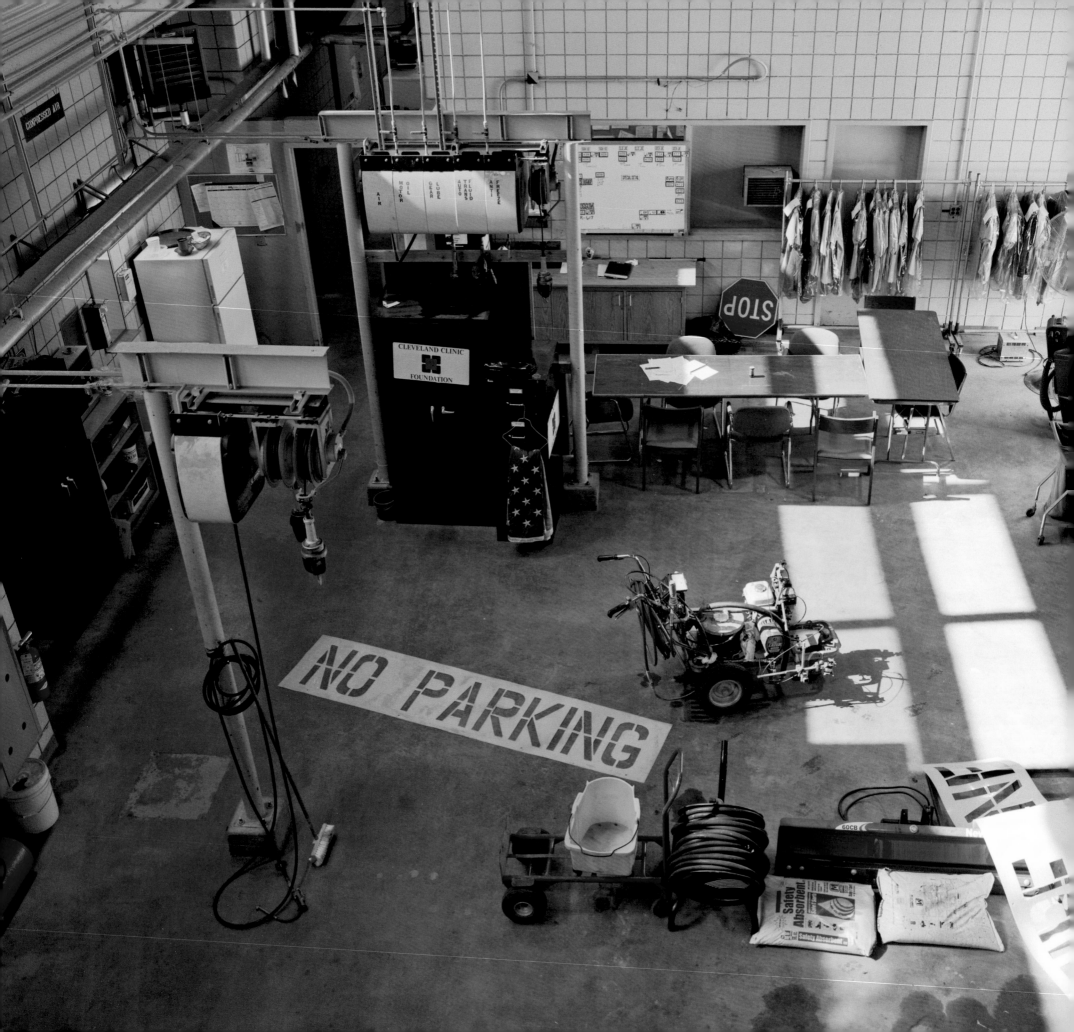

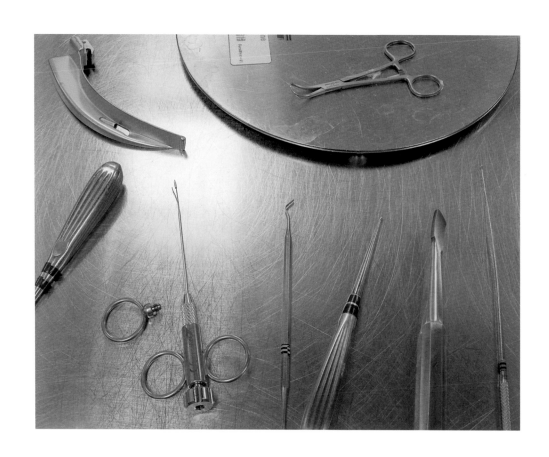

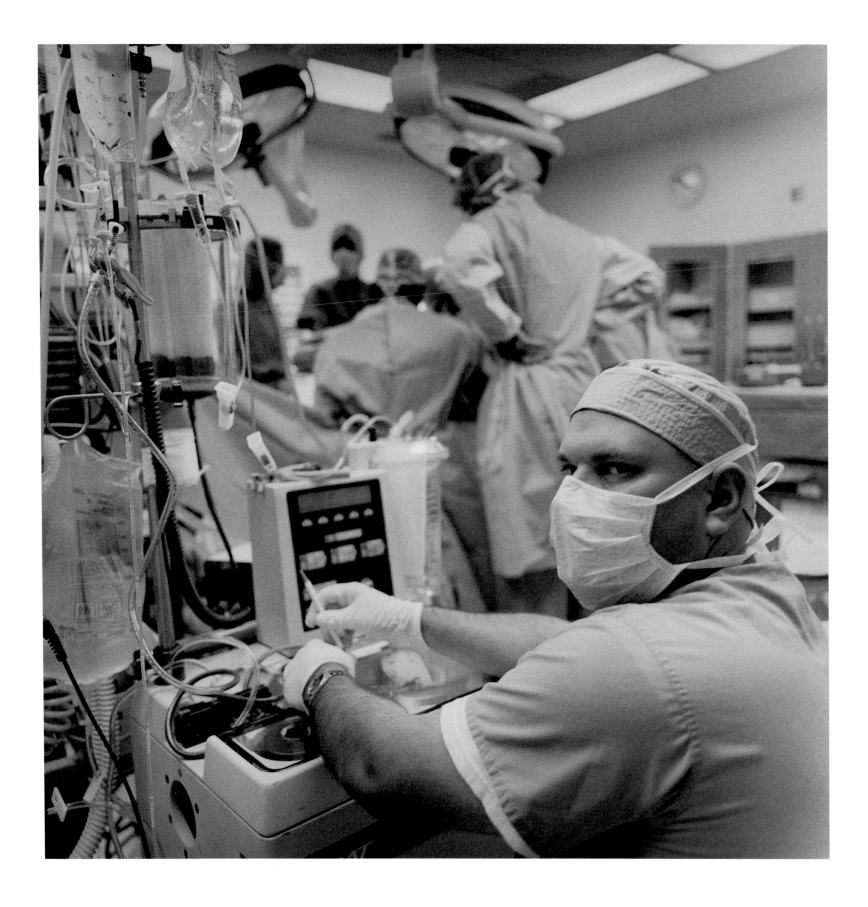

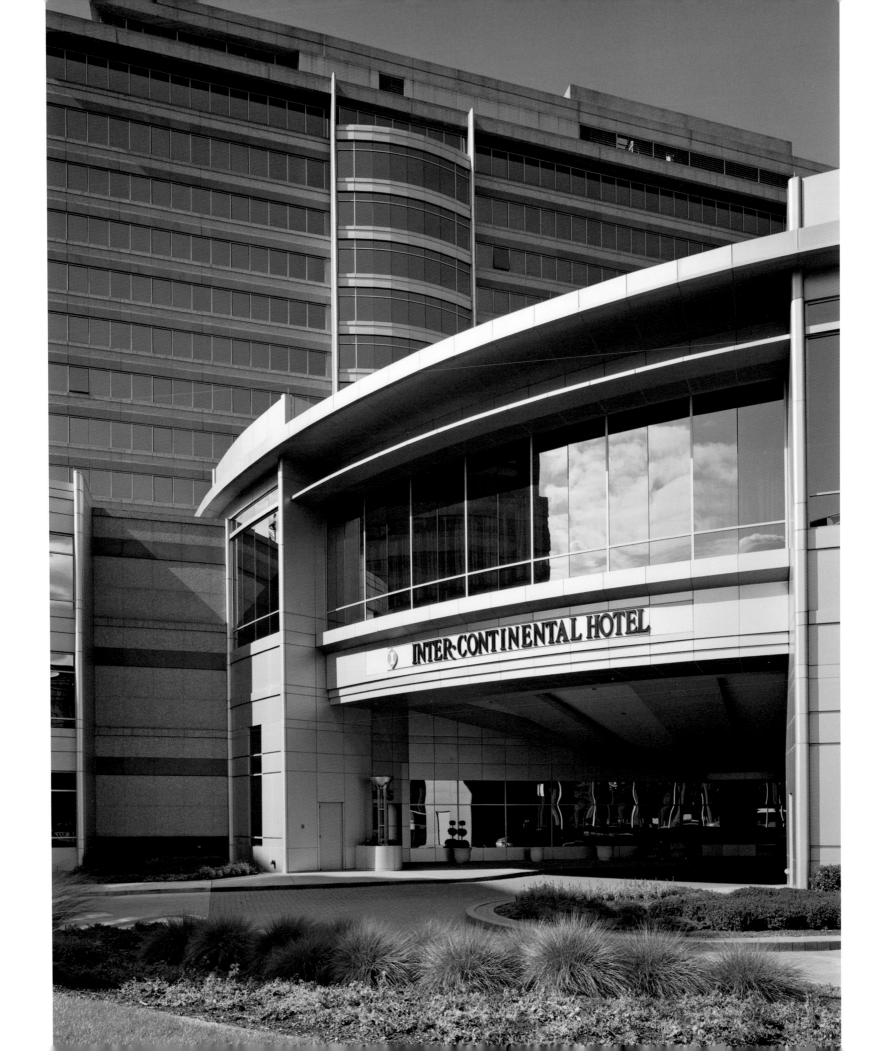

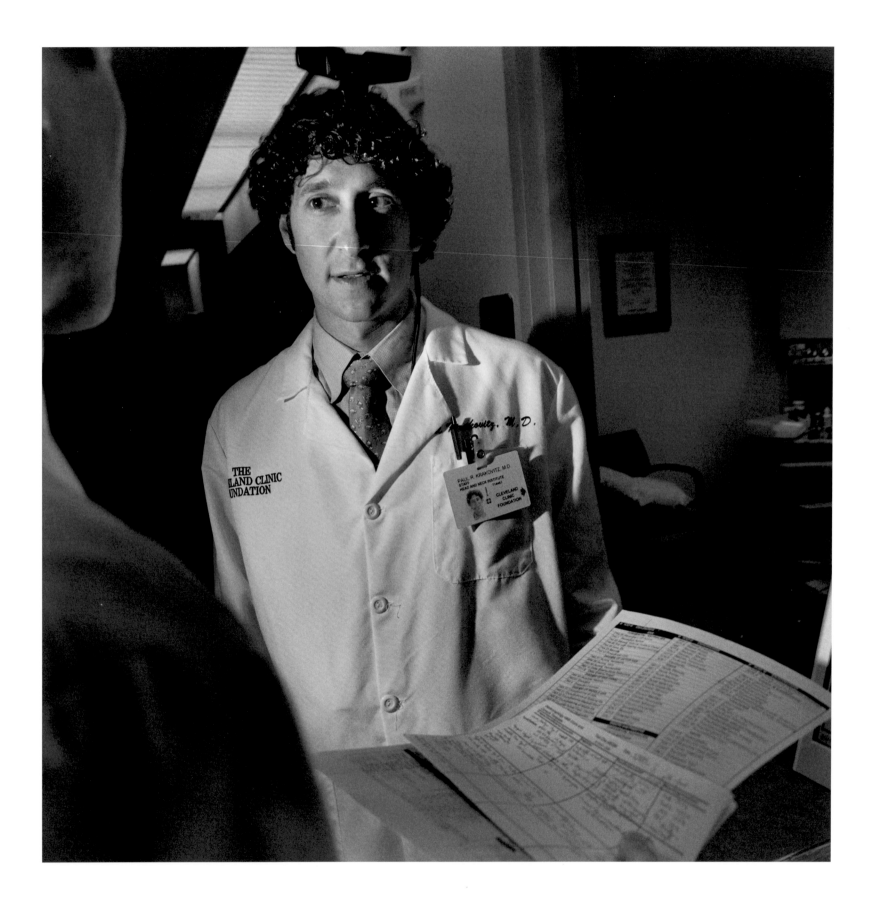

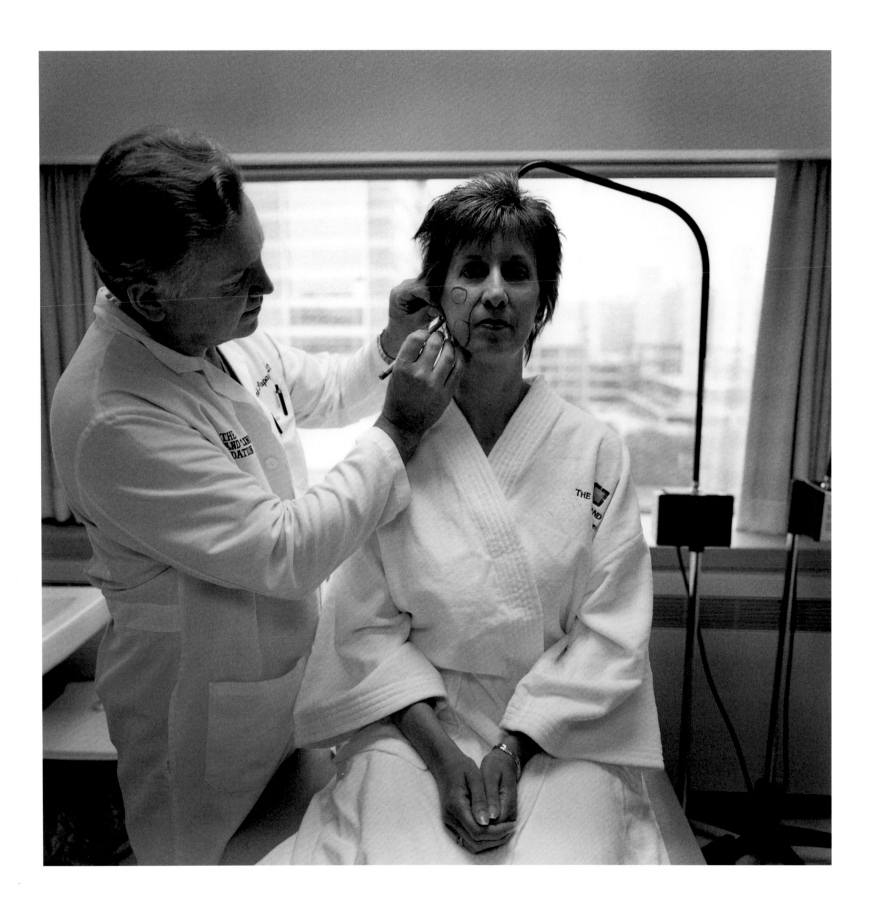

about the project

In late 2005, Cleveland Clinic invited two artists to witness its people, environs and activities over the course of several seasons. Larry Fink and Andrew Moore were chosen for their outstanding abilities and contrasting photographic styles. Larry Fink photographed people. His images are like the stage in a darkened theater. His hand-held flash illuminates the details of the drama, discovering hidden relationships, and revealing the sensitive core of interpersonal life. Andrew Moore photographed places. Made with a tripod camera, his large-scale images reveal a sensibility intensely engaged with architecture, painting and history. They balance formality and complexity, in highly nuanced compositions of light, color and acutely rendered detail. With unprecedented access over a period of 12 months, the two photographers roamed from rooftop to basement, streetside to bedside, in quest of insights and images. Chance and opportunity governed their choice of places and subjects. While *Two Views* includes the worlds of medicine, art, science and architecture, it is not a comprehensive record, but rather an impressionistic overview of a Cleveland Clinic at a moment in time, hard at work putting patients first.

COVER Andrew Moore (detail), Dawn light strikes the Crile Building

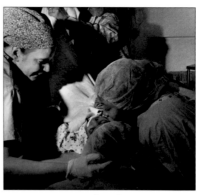

BACK COVER Larry Fink (detail), A family member accompanying a child to surgery plants a kiss at the door to the operating room

PAGE 8 Greeters stand in the main entrance of the Cole Eye Institute
PAGE 9 Looking west across Cleveland Clinic campus, with downtown Cleveland in the distance

PAGE 10 Modern, temporary main entrance beneath the art deco façade of the S building
PAGE 11 The northwest stairwell of Lerner Research Institute lights up as dusk falls

PAGE 12 Oncologist Brian Rini, M.D., confers with a colleague at the Glickman Urological Institute
PAGE 13 Cardiology fellows discuss patient test results in the Heart and Vascular Institute

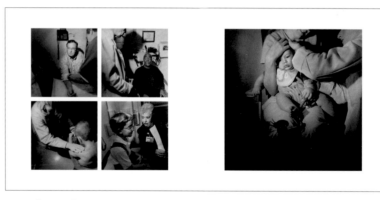

PAGE 14 Syncope Clinic; Head and Neck Institute; Pediatric Hematology and Oncology; Children's Hospital
PAGE 15 A mother holds her child for a hearing test in Audiology

PAGE 16 A dawn view across the lawn at the Cole Eye Institute
PAGE 17 The sinuous northern face of the Taussig Cancer Center at rush hour

PAGE 18 Alumni Library in the Lerner Research Institute, with custom-designed light fixtures
PAGE 19 Former HealthSpace Cleveland on Euclid Avenue—now part of Cleveland Clinic

PAGE 20 Cardiac surgery nurses gather for a brief meeting before beginning the day's work
PAGE 21 A family sits with a patient being prepped for eye surgery in the Children's Hospital

PAGE 22 A view of cardiac surgeon Delos M. Cosgrove, M.D., in the operating room
PAGE 23 Retractors expose a spine for straightening; surgeons replace an abdominal aorta with an implant

PAGE 24 After a lecture, medical students gather around an instructor and an anatomical model
PAGE 25 A new father gazes with curiosity and delight at his baby

PAGE 26 Looking south across Cleveland Clinic campus
PAGE 27 An ocular skylight admits sunshine to the lobby of the Cole Eye Institute

PAGE 28 A Persian rug graces the foyer of Foundation House, decorated for winter holidays
PAGE 29 Cole Eye Institute, looking west toward the Miller Family Pavilion construction site

PAGE 30 A wrought iron fixture hangs beside the porte cochere of Foundation House
PAGE 31 Ivy grows up the walls of the 100-year-old Chester Conference Center

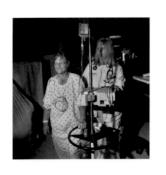

PAGE 32 After cardiac surgery, Gosta Pettersson, M.D., discusses the case with his team
PAGE 33 A patient in a cardiac unit takes a walk with an IV pole and telemetry gear

PAGE 34 Police and Security; Chairman of Education Andrew Fishleder, M.D.; Chief Security Officer Eljay Bowron; meeting planners with Inderbir Gill, M.D.
PAGE 35 President and CEO Delos M. Cosgrove, M.D., at an Executive Team meeting

PAGE 36 Isador Lieberman, M.D., presides over a class learning minimally invasive surgery
PAGE 37 Constance Pytel, RN, BSN, responds to a call in the Emergency Department

 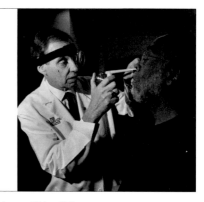

PAGE 40 Chair of Pediatric Hematology/Oncology Joanne Hilden, M.D.
PAGE 41 Marshall Strome, M.D., Chair of the Head and Neck Institute, examines a patient

PAGE 42 Anesthesia resident Pilar Castro, M.D., monitors her patient
PAGE 43 Medical students study hearts in anatomy class

PAGE 44 Balcony view of lobby of the Crile Building, with information desk below
PAGE 45 Vista of Lerner Research Institute, showing courtyard

PAGE 46 The curve of the Cole Eye Institute leads to the W.O. Walker Building
PAGE 47 Interior details of the White Family Mansion

PAGE 48 Studying in the Alumni Library; researchers on break in the George B. Storer Gardens
PAGE 49 Trelliswork atop the Lerner Research Institute

PAGE 50 Research personnel in the lab of Thomas McIntyre, Ph.D., Cell Biology
PAGE 51 An OR surgical technician reaches for an instrument

PAGE 52 Patient, football player, and furry visitor around a table in the Children's Hospital
PAGE 53 Cleveland Browns football player and team mascot meet patients at Children's Hospital

PAGE 54 An employee catches up with her reading in Au Bon Pain restaurant
PAGE 55 Jim Lang in his office at Photographic Services Core of Lerner Research Institute

PAGE 56 Alumni Library; Presidents' portraits; Surgery Center; Prayer Room
PAGE 57 Busy executive assistants in Board of Governors

PAGE 58 Therapeutic massage area beside swimming pool at Children's Hospital Shaker Campus
PAGE 59 A colorful mobile hangs over the stairway in the East 93rd Street Visitors' Garage

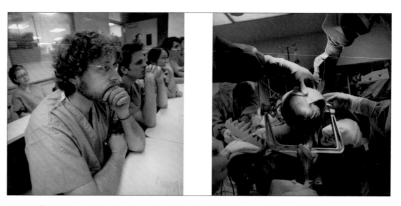

PAGE 60 Students receive instruction in the Cleveland Clinic Lerner College of Medicine
PAGE 61 A surgeon closes an incision in the scalp after brain surgery

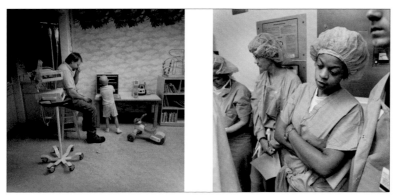

PAGE 62 Father and son share a moment in the playroom of Pediatric Hematology/Oncology
PAGE 63 Tiwanna Williams, RN, BSN, watches a demonstration of a new piece of equipment

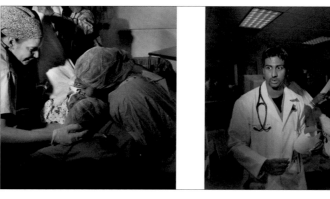

PAGE 64 A family member kisses a pediatric patient before she is taken into surgery
PAGE 65 A resident in the midst of rotation through the Emergency Medicine Department

PAGE 66 Mailboxes outside Biomedical Engineering; flurry of notes
PAGE 67 The first floor lobby of the Taussig Cancer Center mirrors the building's curving front

PAGE 68 Looking north at W.O. Walker Center from Carnegie
PAGE 69 Crile Building, InterContinental Hotel, and F Building on Carnegie, looking north

PAGE 72 The 500-seat MBNA Conference Center located in the InterContinental Hotel
PAGE 73 Euclid Avenue, with Cole Eye Institute (foreground), Crile Building and view of downtown

PAGE 74 The Crile Building outpatient facility, seen in the first light of dawn
PAGE 75 Cranes reflected in curving office windows of the East 93rd Street Visitors' Garage

PAGE 76 Postdoctoral fellow Keiji Kamohara, M.D., peers intently at data
PAGE 77 Visiting surgeons use a model to learn new techniques

PAGE 78 Andrew Novick, M.D., Chairman of the Glickman Urological Institute, confers with a colleague
PAGE 79 Scrubbing up outside the OR in preparation for an obstetric surgery

PAGE 80 An obstetric surgeon and nurse deliver a new baby by cesarean section
PAGE 81 Father, baby and mother bond in the first minutes after delivery

PAGE 82 Construction workers are silhouetted against the S building and Children's Hospital
PAGE 83 A concrete stairway and elevator silos rise above construction of the Miller Family Pavilion

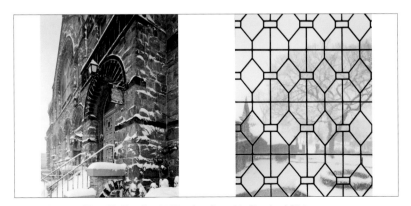

PAGE 84 Exterior of East Mt. Zion Baptist Church, adjacent to Cleveland Clinic campus
PAGE 85 Wintry view through a leaded window onto the courtyard of Foundation House

PAGE 86 A portrait of the late George Crile Jr., M.D., in Foundation House
PAGE 87 Eastern stairwell of Lerner Research Institute with portion of skyway on Carnegie

PAGE 88 Marcia Jackson sorts medications in the Outpatient Pharmacy in the JJ Garage
PAGE 89 Prep Cook Matt Milavec in the Santé Select kitchen

PAGE 90 Translator Naglaa Kamel; Derk Krieger, M.D., Neurology; Chief of Staff Joseph Hahn, M.D.; worker wears protective gear in the Lerner Research Institute
PAGE 91 Jean-Pierre Yared, M.D., Director of the Cardiovascular Intensive Care Unit

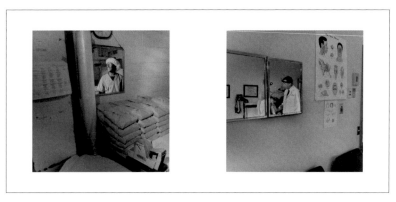

PAGE 92 Dante Howard, Central Services, with packages of sterilized materials ready for delivery
PAGE 93 Marshall Strome, M.D., Chairman of the Head and Neck Institute

PAGE 94 Brand-new plastic piping winds its way through the Power Plant
PAGE 95 Valves serve the massive steam pipes delivering warmth to the main hospital area

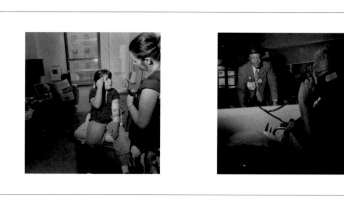

PAGE 96 Special laminar-flow operating rooms reduce the possibility of infection in orthopaedic surgery
PAGE 97 A courtesy cart pauses on a balcony in the Cole Eye Institute

PAGE 98 Nurse Practitioner Holly Clark, ND, RN, CPNP, with a young patient
PAGE 99 Greeter Robert McIntyre is a cheerful presence at the Taussig Cancer Center

PAGE 100 Outside Cardiac Surgery; scene in Emergency Services; Hoyt Samuel, Surgical Support Services; Greg Ball and Donald Cheny step aside to allow passage in Laundry
PAGE 101 A meeting in the executive offices

PAGE 104 A young patient at the Taussig Cancer Center
PAGE 105 Anesthesiology resident Jada Reese, M.D., discusses a case after surgery

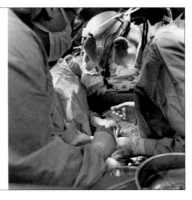

PAGE 106 Edward Cho, M.D., a resident in the Head and Neck Institute
PAGE 107 Cardiac surgeon Gosta Pettersson, M.D., of the Heart and Vascular Institute

PAGE 108 A courtesy cart wends its way from the Cole Eye Institute to the Crile Building
PAGE 109 Skyways meet at the hexagonal stairway tower of the East 100th Street Garage

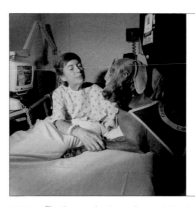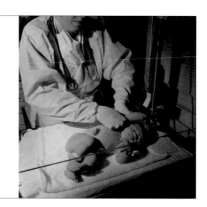

PAGE 110 Police Command Center; sink; Pediatric Dialysis Unit; Minimally Invasive Surgery Classroom
PAGE 111 Tiny video cameras deliver images from inside the patient during laparoscopic surgery

PAGE 112 The therapy dog is a welcome visitor to patients in the Sub-Acute Care Unit
PAGE 113 A newborn is cared for shortly after delivery

PAGE 114 Helping a patient develop his reach at the Children's Hospital Shaker Campus
PAGE 115 Bruce Lytle, M.D., Chairman, Thoracic and Cardiovascular Surgery, in his office

PAGE 116 Charissa Sailes at a cutting board in the Santé Select kitchen
PAGE 117 Stephanie Hagstrom, Ph.D., at a lightbox in the labs of the Cole Eye Institute

PAGE 118 The skyway on Carnegie Avenue links Lerner Research Institute with the Education Wing
PAGE 119 In Textile Care Services, newly embroidered coats are hung in alphabetical order

PAGE 120 Colorful collectibles crowd a researcher's office in the Lerner Research Institute
PAGE 121 Joe Jefferson, Carpentry, amid his and colleagues' work; loading dock, East 93rd Street

  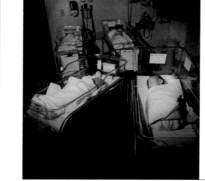 

PAGE 122 Basketball court and running track on top of the W.O. Walker Center
PAGE 123 Steeple of Euclid Avenue Church of God, seen from Foundation House lawn

PAGE 124 Newborns in nursery can be viewed by friends and family through the glass
PAGE 125 Child Life Specialist Tom Richards, BA, CCLS, at the Children's Hospital

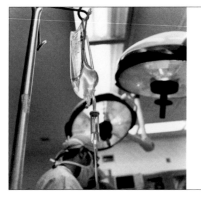 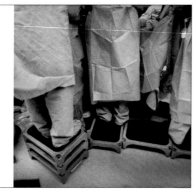  

PAGE 126 An IV bag hangs in an operating room
PAGE 127 Steps enable nurses, assistants, observers and visiting physicians to watch surgery

PAGE 128 The playroom in the Children's Hospital experiences a rare moment of silence
PAGE 129 Four views of rooms and facilities at the Children's Hospital Shaker Campus

PAGE 130 The East 93rd Street Visitors' Garage seen from the front of the White Family Mansion
PAGE 131 Late afternoon sun shines on the west-facing wall of the Cole Eye Institute

PAGE 132 An array of tools and devices in orthopaedic surgery
PAGE 133 Liquids lined up in the Dialysis Unit; sterile sheets are neatly packaged

PAGE 136 Helicopter view of the Miller Family Pavilion construction site, facing southeast
PAGE 137 Crile Building outpatient facility, seen from Campus green

PAGE 138 A caduceus is at the center of a metalwork grill
PAGE 139 Staircase of Foundation House with statuette of George Crile Sr., M.D., on table

PAGE 140 Hilel Lewis, M.D., Chairman of the Cole Eye Institute, examines a patient
PAGE 141 A patient's hand is visible beneath sterile sheets as surgeons operate

PAGE 142 A young pitcher is wired in Sports Medicine's Throw Right Baseball Program
PAGE 143 The Throw Right Baseball Program videotapes, measures and analyzes movements
 to reduce pitching injuries

PAGE 144 Cleveland Clinic aerial view with Crile Building in foreground, Lake Erie on horizon
PAGE 145 Case Western Reserve University, foreground, with Epworth Euclid Church, Cleveland Clinic,
 looking southwest

PAGE 146 Storage Garage, W.O. Walker Center, with traffic signs, uniforms and tools
PAGE 147 Stainless steel is the predominant texture in sterile processing

 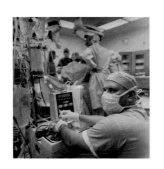

PAGE 148 Medical students gather around a demonstration in the anatomy lab
PAGE 149 IAT Lead Daniel Bishop collects cells for autotransfusion, a blood-sparing technique

PAGE 150 When the rain stops, work resumes on the Miller Family Pavilion
PAGE 151 Workers and machinery at sites of the Miller Family Pavilion and Glickman Tower

PAGE 152 Cleveland Clinic security personnel guard the entrance to the construction site on
 Euclid Avenue
PAGE 153 Tammy Owings, Ph.D., straps a student in a chair for a weightlessness experiment

PAGE 154 Outside the Children's Hospital Shaker Campus, a special wheelchair swing awaits use
PAGE 155 The InterContinental Hotel has 12 stories and 300 rooms, plus a Presidential Suite

 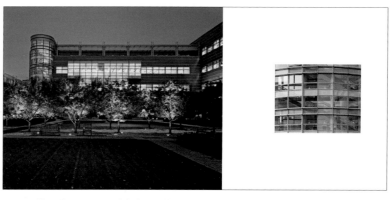

PAGE 156 A skeleton is used for reference in the Center for Medical Art and Photography
PAGE 157 Construction cranes spin behind the "Four in One" sculpture on the Campus Green

PAGE 158 The education wing of the Lerner Research Institute comes alight at dusk
PAGE 159 Stairways are visible through the glass from outside the Lerner Research Institute

  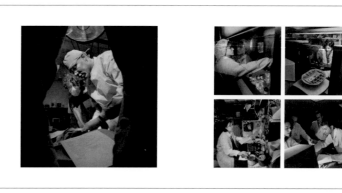

PAGE 160 Paul Krakovitz, M.D., practices pediatric otolaryngology in the Head and Neck Institute
PAGE 161 Plastic surgeon Frank Papay, M.D., shows how he marks a patient before facial surgery

PAGE 162 After a lecture, Lerner College of Medicine students learn from an anatomical model
PAGE 163 Jill Spuzzillo, CPT, Taussig Cancer Center; Cell Biology fellow Tammy Bhattacharyya, M.D.; Technologist Ivanda Pavlovska, Molecular Genetics; residents confer

PAGE 164 Julie Niezgoda, M.D., Chairman of Pediatric Anesthesiology, returns a page between surgeries
PAGE 165 Cleveland Clinic Police and Security offices

PAGE 178 Salad Prep; supply room, Children's Hospital; Fred Lautzenhieser, Archives; dialysis fluids
PAGE 179 View from researcher's office; Plastic Surgery; outstanding fellows; paper tower on desktop

LARRY FINK has been a professional photographer for 45 years. The recipient of two John Simon Guggenheim Memorial Foundation Fellowships and two National Endowment for the Arts grants, he has had one-man shows at The Museum of Modern Art, the Whitney Museum of American Art, the San Francisco Museum of Art, the Musée de la Lausanne Photographie in Belgium and the Musée de l'Elysée in Switzerland, among others. He has gallery shows in New York, Los Angeles and Paris. In 2002, Fink received an honorary degree of Doctor of Fine Arts from the College for Creative Studies in Detroit, Michigan. He has seven books published: *Social Graces* (1984), *Boxing* (1997), *Runway* (2000), a second publication of *Social Graces* (2001) with additional images, *Forbidden Pictures* (2004), the retrospective *Larry Fink* (2005), *Primal Elegance* (2006), and a book of music images *Somewhere There's Music* (2006). His commercial work includes advertising campaigns for Smirnoff, Bacardi and Cunard Lines (Q.E.2). His work has appeared in top publications including *Vanity Fair, W, GQ, Detour, The New York Times Magazine* and *The New Yorker*. He has been teaching for the past 41 years, the last 16 years as a professor of photography at Bard College.

ANDREW MOORE is a fine art photographer and filmmaker. His photographs are featured in the collections of the Whitney Museum of American Art, Yale University Art Gallery, the Library of Congress, the Israel Museum, the High Museum of Art, George Eastman House and the Canadian Centre for Architecture. Moore has won grants from the National Endowment for the Humanities, New York State Council on the Arts and private foundations. His books include *Inside Havana* (2002), *Governor's Island* (2004) and *Russia* (2005). He was producer and cinematographer for the documentary *How to Draw a Bunny*—awarded a special jury prize at the Sundance Film Festival. Moore is a visiting lecturer on digital photography at Princeton University and teaches in the Photography MFA program at the School of Visual Arts in New York City. In 2006 he was artist-in-residence at Dartmouth College. His show at Dartmouth was followed by exhibitions at Yancey Richardson Gallery in New York City and the Museum of Russian Art in Minneapolis. His 2007 projects include a book on the projects of Robert Moses and exhibition in three parts at Columbia University, the Museum of the City of New York, and the Queens Museum of Art; and a major retrospective at the Reflex Gallery in Amsterdam.

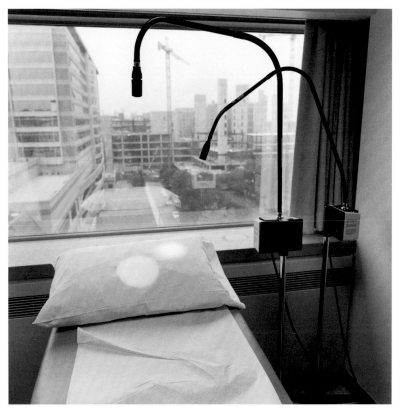

CREATIVE DIRECTOR

Mark Schwartz, Nesnadny + Schwartz

DESIGNERS

Dana Ross and Stacie Ross, Nesnadny + Schwartz

TEXT

Steve Szilagyi, Cleveland Clinic

DIGITAL SEPARATIONS AND PRINTING

Meridian Printing, Coordinated by Daniel Frank

BINDING

Acme Bookbinding

COMPOSITION

News Gothic

COATED PAPER

Creator 100# Silk Text, by Torraspapel